DOG BOOK

The complete book of dog and puppy care

Written by Veterinary Surgeons
Illustrated by Judy Friedlander and Gillian Croucher

For further information, contact Sherley's at Beaphar UK Ltd,
Homefield Road, Haverhill, Suffolk, CB9 8QP, Telephone: (01440) 715700
www.sherleys.com

ABOUT THIS BOOK

Of all the animals that have been domesticated, the dog is the most popular pet. Since primitive man first tamed the ancestor of today's dogs, an enormous variety of breeds has been evolved. Aspiring dog owners now have a wide choice of shape, colour and character, whether they are looking for a loving companion or a wiling workmate.

But whatever breed is chosen or already owned, the basic principles of dog care and management remain the same. For nearly one hundred years the name Sherley's has been associated with the health and welfare of Britain's pets and with dog care in particular. During this time, the Sherley's Dog book has become perhaps the best known work of its kind and has been distributed all over the world.

The Sherley's Dog Book is written by Veterinary Surgeons and is frequently revised to keep it as up-to-date as possible in the light of modern knowledge and practice. The book is designed to provide a complete guide to keeping a dog, from birth to old age, in health and during illness. The first four chapters are devoted to choosing, breeding, rearing and looking after dogs. They are written with a sympathetic understanding of a dog's behavioural characteristics, so that the owner and the dog can obtain the best from each other.

The last four chapters are concerned primarily with the health of dogs and cover parasites, treatment, first aid and illness, together with a description of Sherley's dog care products. As a result of the therapeutic revolution, veterinary medicine, like human medicine, has moved away from the symptomatic towards a specific treatment and prevention of diseases, using new and powerful medicines. Due emphasis is given to the increasingly important role that the Veterinary Surgeon can play in keeping dogs fit and healthy. The very significant part that the owner can take in recognising symptoms, treating more minor conditions, and in nursing a sick dog, is also fully covered.

Sherley's also publish the Sherley's Cat Book – a complete manual for every cat owner and breeder.

CHAPTER		Page

50th Edition 2002

Printed in the Netherlands by Hassink Drukkers B.V. - Haaksbergen.

CHOOSING AND KNOWING YOUR DOG

Since the earliest days of man's civilisation the dog has been his friend and companion. Undoubtedly the dog was at first a guard and a hunter, but he very soon moved into the house and became one of the family. In Britain, above all countries, we consider ourselves a nation of animal lovers, so when the time comes for you to choose your new pet, make sure that you do so for the right reasons.

Unfortunately, too many dogs that are initially taken in by prospective owners end up being destroyed because they do not fit in with the owners and their lifestyle. Most of the time it is the fault of the owners who do not give enough consideration to the responsibility that owning a pet brings. If we gave more thought to choosing the right pet and learning how to care for it properly, this sad situation could be greatly improved.

THE RIGHT DOG FOR YOU

If you are really attracted to one particular breed, and interested in showing and breeding, the situation is already decided for you. You will select the dog of your choosing, the right pet, and then make whatever changes are necessary in your way of life to suit it. However, for most of us the dog is a pet, a companion, and a very important member of the family. It is well worth spending a little time to find the dog which will fit most comfortably into your home.

PEDIGREE OR CROSS-BREED?

If you buy a pedigree puppy you have a general idea of the shape and size which you can expect in the adult, whereas a mongrel puppy is perhaps more of a gamble. One thing is certain, pedigree or mongrel, you are going to think your dog is the best in the world.

Choosing the puppy

It should be remembered though, that as a result of in-breeding over the years to produce show "characteristics", some of the breeds now possess inherited defects. An example of this is hip dysplasia in some of the larger breeds, retinal atrophy (a form of blindness) in Labradors, and a tendency to joint abnormalities in Poodles, Pekes and Pugs. It is important to buy your pedigree pup from a reputable breeder. Many poor specimens are sold, especially through dealers, and a certificate of pedigree is not a guarantee of health or soundness. On the other hand, the idea that mongrels are hardier, or more resistant to disease is simply an old wives' tale. There is no difference at all in the resistance of pedigrees or crossbreeds, and each requires equal care from their owners. Many mongrels, especially the Poodles or small terrier crosses, make charming and intelligent pets, but care should be taken over the larger cross-breeds such as German Shepherd dogs and Rottweillers, as they sometimes seem to inherit the aggressive features of each parent.

DOG OR BITCH?

Which sex?

People tend to think that a dog is less trouble to keep than a bitch, but this is not necessarily so. A bitch comes in season for three weeks approximately every six months and must of course be carefully watched, and kept in. A dog, however, retains its interest in the opposite sex all the year round and if not restrained may start to wander off in search of females, becoming a nuisance and a danger on the roads. In addition, bitches often seem to have sweeter dispositions and make better pets especially where there are children in the house.

The skeleton of the dog

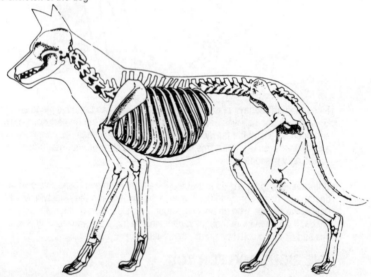

NEUTERING

Both dogs and bitches, like cats, can be neutered and in view of the present population explosion in the dog world it is very well worth considering, not only for your own convenience, but for the social good.

The operation in either case is carried out under a general anaesthetic. It does not change the animals' character (for good or for bad) and contrary to popular opinion it does not make the animal fat, provided careful attention to diet and exercise is maintained. A bitch which has been sterilised does not come on heat or attract other dogs and is an ideal companion.

Do not be deterred if you cannot afford neutering. Many animal charities now help cover the cost of such operations, in an attempt to reduce the number of unwanted pets.

However, if you feel reluctant to consider an operation there are now tablets and injections available which greatly reduce the nuisance of the heat period.

THE RIGHT SIZE OF DOG

Large or small?

However much you may love the thought of a big dog, do think seriously before buying one. Certainly a big dog is a deterrent to burglars, but a small one with a big bark may do as much good. To be an effective guard, a dog must be properly trained or you may soon find yourself in trouble when he mistakes the postman for an intruder. Obviously, if you live in a flat or town house you are going to have problems with a large dog, but even in the country a big dog must be exercised, and not allowed to wander and cause danger to livestock. Training is of particular importance with large dogs, as many, from lack of early training, get beyond their owners' control, and may even have to be destroyed. Big dogs need big fences to keep them in, and very big food bills if they are to be fed properly, so unless your circumstances really justify it, think first, and choose a dog that is just the right size for you.

HOW TO BE A GOOD OWNER

Before making the decision about buying a new puppy, here are some points you should consider:

Is someone at home for most of the day? A dog, especially a puppy, should not be left on its own for more than a few hours at a time. If you are out at work from nine to five, don't get a dog, unless you can make really satisfactory arrangements with a neighbour to let it out.

Holiday expenses

What about holidays? It is sad to say that more dogs are destroyed at holiday time than at any other. Unless you have a helpful family to look after your dog, be prepared for the expense of kennels. Because of the increase in cost of labour and food, reputable kennels now have to make a high charge – and don't forget to book well ahead.

Recognise the costs

Are you prepared for the cost of keeping a dog? This includes not only the cost of food, and kennels at holiday time, but also the cost of vaccination against the major diseases (this is something which every conscientious owner must have done) and also possible veterinary fees in case of illness. A dog, like a child, can be ill quite suddenly and unexpectedly and there is as yet no National Health Service for dogs, although various welfare organisations such as the RSPCA and PDSA will provide help for those who are in difficult circumstances and unable to afford veterinary fees. Canine insurance policies are growing in popularity and can prove a great help in cases of accident or sudden illness, but they do not pay for the cost of routine treatments such as vaccination or neutering. Be sure to read the policy thoroughly and be certain that you understand the terms of the protection offered. Most Veterinary Surgeons can supply details of these policies and how to enrol.

Plenty of exercise

Exercise. To keep healthy and happy, dogs need daily exercise, which means a good run off the lead in a field or park, or a game with a ball, not just a stroll round to the shops on a lead. If you love your dog, be prepared to sacrifice some of your leisure time each day, whatever the weather. If your health or circumstances really do not allow you to provide this type of exercise, consider giving a home to an older dog. Your local RSPCA or lost dogs' home may have just the right one for you.

Puppies and children

Family circumstances. Dogs and children usually love each other and get on well, but do not make the mistake of buying a young puppy for a toddler. Young children can be thoughtlessly cruel and a puppy may be badly pulled about, worse still a young puppy's bones may be easily broken if a child thinks it can be treated like the other cuddly toys. Wait until the children are older and a little more responsible. They will get much more pleasure out of a dog when they are old enough to take it for walks.

Grooming. If you do not have much time to spare, choose a dog with a smooth or wire coat,

Regular grooming

which needs little attention to keep it tidy. Long and curly coated dogs look beautiful, but they need daily grooming to keep them this way. Poodles need regular trimming, as well as grooming, so unless you are able to do this yourself be prepared for extra expense.

The library is a good source of information on individual breeds, or consult the specialist dog magazines.

BUYING A DOG

A careful choice

Never buy a puppy or older dog on impulse or a whim. It is best to buy directly from the breeder whenever possible. Visit the home of the breeder, or the owner of the bitch. You will be able to ensure that your pup came from a clean and healthy home, and you may get helpful advice about the kind of diet and training that your pup has been used to.

Dogs' home

Never buy a pup through a newspaper advertisement, without seeing it first. It may have been reared on a puppy farm, and have been ill-treated or be diseased. With no demand, puppy farms will eventually go out of business. A dog rescue home is a good place to buy an older dog. You will have the satisfaction of feeling that you are saving a life and giving an unloved pet a new home. However, don't just fall for the first dog that you see (and it can be very hard not to), but talk to the officials at the home and try to find out a little of the background; how old is the dog, has it been ill, and what is its temperament like.

CHOOSING A HEALTHY PUP

It is often difficult for a beginner to distinguish a healthy pup from a poor one – to them one attractive little bundle of fur looks much like another – but really there is all the difference in the world. A healthy pup should be plump, but not have a swollen or blown-up stomach. Its skin should be loose and pick up easily, because there is a healthy layer of fat under the skin (instead of seeming to stick to the bones). The coat should shine (except in the case of wire-haired varieties) and of course should be free of fleas and lice.

The eyes should be bright and free from any sign of discharge. In addition it is wise to choose a pup which is lively and readily comes to greet people. A timid or withdrawn type of pup may have a problem personality and be difficult to train. Finally, don't be surprised if a conscientious dog breeder wants to ask a lot of questions to find out if you are going to be a suitable person to own one of his pups.

Dogs are no longer required to be licensed, as they once were. However, it remains a requirement of the law that all dogs should wear a collar, with a nametag showing your address. This is obviously of the greatest importance, as if your pup should stray, or become involved in an accident, it can be reunited with you. Dogs can also be tattooed with an identity number and this does much to reduce the number of strays. A more modern approach to dog registration is the painless introduction of a microchip under the skin of the dog which has a record of the owner's name and address. This can be read by a special scanning machine. Contact your local Veterinary Surgeon for details about either tattooing or the microchip identification method.

An alternative idea is the Sherley's Lost and Found Flea Collar. Each collar is printed with a unique identity number, and Sherley's Freephone number. Having fitted the new flea collar to your pet, register the number with Sherley's straight away. If your dog should wander, the finder can ring Sherley's free of charge, and we can reunite you with your pet straight away. At the end of the collar's active life you will receive a reminder card from Sherley's. Simply fit a new collar and advise Sherley's of the change in number.

Under the 1993 Dangerous Dogs Act, it is now illegal to purchase the following breeds: - Pitbull Terrier, Japanese Tosa, Fila Braziliero, and the Dogo Argentino.

Following this act, owners of such breeds had to have their pets registered with the Police, neutered, and microchipped.

oad safety

On some roads, dogs are required to be kept on a lead at all times. This is mainly to prevent road accidents. However, with the ever increasing traffic problem, no conscientious owner should allow a pet to wander in the streets, for its own sake.

If you live in the countryside take special care that your dog does not wander away on its own. Dogs cause terrible damage each year to sheep and lambs, and a dog may be shot by a farmer if it is seen in suspicious circumstances.

ollution

Pollution is now a great problem in the world. Take care that your dog never fouls the footpath, or other public areas. The penalty in some districts may be as much as £100 or more, and it is the duty of all dog lovers to see that their pets do not cause annoyance to the rest of the world. There are many clever devices that can perform the very necessary task of removing dog faeces. See your local pet shop or Veterinary Surgeon for details.

Points of the dog – technical terms

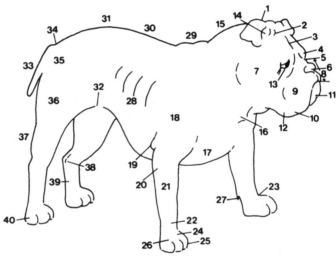

(1)	Apex of skull	(16)	Dewlap	(31)	Loin
(2)	Skull	(17)	Brisket	(32)	Belly
(3)	Groove	(18)	Shoulder	(33)	Tail
(4)	Temples or frontal bones	(19)	Elbow	(34)	Set of tail or stern
(5)	Stop	(20)	Calf	(35)	Hip joint
(6)	Nose	(21)	Forearm	(36)	Thigh
(7)	Cheek	(22)	Knee	(37)	Stifle
(8)	Layback	(23)	Pastern	(38)	Hock
(9)	Cushion	(24)	Fore-paws	(39)	Pastern
(10)	Chop or flews	(25)	Toes	(40)	Hind-paws
(11)	Lowerjaw	(26)	Knuckles		
(12)	Corner of the jaw	(27)	Dew-claw		
(13)	Corner of the eye	(28)	Ribs		
(14)	Set of ear	(29)	Wither		
(15)	Neck	(30)	Back		

TABLE OF DIFFERENT BREEDS AND SUITABILITY

This table lists some (but not all) of the most popular breeds of dogs and indicates the adult size (L = large, M = medium and S = small), a general guide to the weight of adult dogs, suitability to children and amount of grooming and exercise required. Remember that this is for guidance only - some breeds will have small and large varieties in the breed (i.e. Poodles, Dachshunds, etc.) and that individual temperament and training will reflect in the characters of all dogs. For further information consult your library, or the relevant breed society.

Breed	Size	Adult weight (lbs)	Suitability for children	Grooming required	Exercise needed
Afghan	L	50-60	Excellent	Much	Some
Airedale	L	40-50	Good	Some	Much
Basset	M	25-45	Excellent	Minimal	Minimal
Beagle	S	18-30	Good	Minimal	Some
Boxer	L	62-66	Good	Minimal	Much
Bulldog	M	40-50	Excellent	Minimal	Minimal
Cairn	S	13-14	Good	Some	Some
Cavalier King Charles Spaniel	S	10-15	Good	Some	Some
Chihuahua	S	2-6	Not recommended	Minimal	Minimal
Chow chow	M	50-55	Not recommended	Much	Some
Cocker Spaniel	M	25-28	Excellent	Much	Some
Collie	L	40-65	Excellent	Some	Some
Dachshund	S	7-20	Good	Minimal	Minimal
Dalmation	L	55-60	Excellent	Minimal	Some
Dobermann	L	65-90	Not recommended	Minimal	Much

Breed	Size	Weight	Children		
English Springer Spaniel	M	45-50	Excellent	Much	Much
Fox Terrier	S	15-19	Excellent	Minimal	Some
German Shepherd	L	75-85	Good	Some	Much
Great Dane	L	120-150	Excellent	Some	Some
Irish Setter	M	50-60	Good	Some	Much
Old English Sheepdog	L	50-90	Excellent	Much	Much
Pekinese	S	7-12	Not recommended	Much	Minimal
Pembroke corgi	S	18-24	Good	Minimal	Some
Poodle	S	8-15	Good	Much	Some
Pug	S	14-18	Good	Minimal	Minimal
Retriever	L	55-70	Excellent	Some	Much
Labrador Retriever	L	55-70	Excellent	Some	Much
Scottish Terrier	S	18-22	Not recommended	Some	Some
Shetland Sheepdog	M	16-18	Excellent	Much	Some
Shih Tzu	S	10-16	Good	Much	Minimal
Staffordshire Bull Terrier	M	40-60	Good	Minimal	Some
West Highland White Terrier	S	12-19	Good	Much	Minimal
Whippet	M	10-28	Good	Minimal	Much
Yorkshire Terrier	S	4-8	Good	Much	Minimal

CHAPTER 2

BREEDING AND REARING DOGS

Rearing a litter of puppies can be a delightful and rewarding experience, but it should not be undertaken without a great deal of serious thought. Even assuming that you love dogs, and will consider the hard work involved as no disadvantage, it is sadly true that there are already far more dogs in the world than there are kind and welcoming homes to take them. In other words, dogs too are suffering from a population explosion.

Family planning

There is a popular idea that it does a dog or bitch good to be mated, but there is no evidence whatsoever to support this. The dog which tends to be oversexed will not be improved by being used once or twice at stud. Some bitches make excellent mothers and obviously enjoy maternity, but for others it can be a difficult and painful experience. There is no evidence that having a litter of pups has a beneficial effect on either the health or the temperament of a bitch, and one would very much doubt if the ordinary, happy family pet ever feels that she is unlucky to have been deprived of the chance to rear a litter. By all means rear a litter of pups if you really want them, and be sure to find good homes for them all, but do not just because you feel you should.

Should you breed from your dog?

If you own a bitch, you should think very seriously about having her spayed. The operation is reasonably simple, relatively painless, and safe. Your dog can be successfully neutered at any time in its life, but to avoid the risk of unwanted pregnancies, it should be done at the earliest possible age. Ideally, this will be before the bitch's first season, which occurs between 8 and 18 months. Your Veterinary Surgeon will advise on the best age.

If you do not have your bitch spayed, she will come into "season"(i.e. be fertile, and very attractive to male dogs) twice yearly, each time for a period of 3 weeks. If you do not intend to breed from her, it is much simpler and more sensible to have her spayed.

BREEDING PEDIGREE PUPS

Do not go into dog breeding in the expectation of making money. The idea of selling a large litter at a high price may sound inviting, but the cost of rearing puppies properly can be considerable, and there are many pitfalls on the way. Your bitch may have only one or two pups, or may lie on a beautiful litter and kill them, or she may need a caesarean operation which will leave you well out of pocket.

Choosing the breed

Try to choose a popular breed which will sell well. One of the small but sturdy varieties is wisest for the beginner, such as corgis, miniature poodles, cairns or west highlands. The tiny or toy breeds like chihuahuas, pekes or toy poodles can be difficult to whelp and delicate to rear.

Labradors are popular and can have large litters, but if several bitches whelp at about the same time the market in your district may become rather flooded and eight or nine unsaleable pups can eat a great deal of food. If you have good pups it is worth advertising in one of the dog papers as well as in your local press.

Buying your dogs

Many people, when planning to start breeding dogs, go out and buy a bitch and a dog. While this sounds reasonable it is not really a practical idea. Your bitch will come in season twice a year and it is obviously not kind or sensible to breed from her each season. You will then have to board one of the dogs out, or suffer all the inconvenience of trying to keep them apart. It is much wiser to buy two bitches and then when the time comes, select a suitable stud dog, and preferably one that is known to be producing good litters with the characteristics you hope to see in your pups. It is even less of a gamble to consider buying an adult bitch which has already had one successful litter, but unfortunately these are the very bitches which breeders want to keep.

THE STUD DOG

Fees and terms

The owner of a stud dog will charge a fee for the mating, and the amount may vary greatly with the pedigree and show reputation of the dog. Sometimes an arrangement may be reached whereby the owner of the stud will agree to take the pup which is "the pick of the litter" instead of payment at the time of mating. Usually, if the mating is unsuccessful and there are no puppies the owner of the stud dog may allow you to bring your bitch back at the next season without charge, but this is something that the two parties concerned must decide for themselves, and it is best that it is put in writing.

KEEPING A STUD DOG

If you are interested in showing, and if your dog is proving successful and winning prizes you may find that people ask you if they can use your dog at stud, that is to say, mating him to suitable bitches. Obviously, you can charge a fee but the amount will depend on the quality of your dog. A stud dog should be healthy and fit and should receive a good balanced diet, but there is no need to give him any particular elaborate diet. It is not desirable that he should be overweight.

MONORCHIDS OR CRYPTORCHIDS

These are dogs in which one, or both testicles have been retained in the abdomen. They are able to breed, but should not be used at stud, as they may pass on the fault to their pups. The retained testicles should be surgically removed by your Veterinary Surgeon as there is an increased risk of them becoming cancerous in later life.

BREEDING TERMS

Sometimes if the prospective buyer is unable to afford to pay for a bitch at the time, a breeder may suggest selling it on "breeding terms". This means that the breeder will be entitled to half of one or more litters. While this may sound tempting it is better to stop and think. It may work out well, but your dog will not be truly your own for a long time and it can lead to difficulties and disagreements.

RECOGNITION OF HEAT

In most cases the first sign of heat (or season or oestrus) is that your bitch becomes very interesting to any male dog that you may happen to meet.

You will probably notice that there is marked swelling of the vulva (the external genital opening) and this becomes noticeable up to the twelfth to fourteenth day after onset of heat. There is usually a clear or whitish discharge which later becomes blood-stained. It may sometimes happen that the first indication you get is when you notice a few spots of blood on the floor.

There is considerable difference in the amount of evidence of heat which different bitches show. In some it may pass almost unnoticed (so the owner must take special care), while in others there is considerable bleeding. A season usually lasts about twenty-one days, but care should be taken after this time if dogs still seem to be interested.

MANAGEMENT OF THE BITCH IN SEASON

Many people feel apprehensive about owning a bitch for the first time because of the supposed problems when they come into season. This is a pity as today there are many quite efficient ways of dealing with the situation, and often bitches tend to have sweeter dispositions and make better pets.

SURGICAL STERILISATION – SPAYING

Spaying

This is the most effective and permanent method, and is advisable in any case where you have decided quite definitely that you do not want pups in the future. The operation can be carried out before or after the first season depending on your Veterinary Surgeon's preference.

The operation requires a general anaesthetic and your bitch will need a little extra care and nursing for a period of about one week. After the operation, the bitch will be free from all the symptoms of heat, and also free from the "false pregnancy" symptoms which sometimes follow. There are no adverse effects on the health or the temperament of the bitch (indeed, the guide dogs for the blind are always spayed). Provided careful attention is given to diet and exercise, spayed bitches should not put on weight.

TABLETS OR INJECTIONS

This temporary method, which must be carried out under the supervision of a Veterinary Surgeon, can be very successful in preventing or postponing the season, though it may not always prevent the occurrence of false pregnancy. It is useful for people who may want to breed from their bitch later, or for postponing a season which might interfere with a show or holiday.

DEODORANT TABLETS

Controlling 'followers'

If your bitch comes into season before you have had time to consider preventative measures it is most important that she should be kept under strict supervision as soon as any signs of heat are noticed (see Recognition of Heat). Tablets are available from Sherley's, which may help to reduce the nuisance of "followers" on your doorstep, but it is unwise to consider that your own garden is safe, or "dog proof". Male dogs can show amazing ingenuity in getting in, and even a normally timid and home loving bitch may, when in season, attempt to get out in search of a mate.

With a small dog it is always worth carrying her a little way away from the house before exercising her, so that if any dog should, by chance, pick up the scent he will not be led to your front door.

MESALLIANCE OR MIS-MATING

If in spite of all your care your bitch should be mated accidentally, it is possible to prevent conception by the injection of a hormone preparation, provided that it is given within 48 hours. It is best to consult your Veterinary Surgeon as soon as possible. It is sometimes said that a pedigree bitch that has been mis-mated is "spoiled" for further breeding. This is, of course, quite untrue. If she is mated to a pedigree dog at the next season she will produce pedigree pups.

FALSE PREGNANCY

In the period usually between six to eight weeks after a season many bitches will show some symptoms of the condition known as "false pregnancy" although they have not been mated. They may vary from a slight swelling of the milk glands, with the secretion of a little watery fluid, to marked abdominal swelling and the production of large quantities of milk. The psychological symptoms may be even more marked. The bitch becomes restless and may cry a lot. She will usually scratch up her bedding to make a nest for the phantom pups, and in some cases carry a doll or a woolly toy about, and growl in a very possessive way if anyone approaches.
This curious behaviour is only the normal reaction of a bitch to the effect of its hormones. If the symptoms are only slight, there is no need to worry. It is a good idea to take the sufferer out and take her mind off the situation, rather than leaving her to brood in her basket. If the symptoms are very pronounced it is best to consult a Veterinary Surgeon.

MATING YOUR BITCH

Age to mate

Although a bitch may start to come into season from soon after six months, it is not advisable to mate her until she is about eighteen months old. Up to a year old she is still growing and the strain of producing a litter of pups at this time might well retard her development. Ideally she should be in good bodily condition, but not overweight. It is probably wiser not to mate your bitch for the first time any later than at five years old, although there are cases such as the eleven year old terrier that surprised her owner with a healthy first litter. She was obviously an exception to the rule.

THE RIGHT TIME

Ten days after the commencement of the season is usually considered to be the right time to mate a bitch, but as it is quite difficult for an inexperienced person to be sure which was the first day, it is probably safer to say somewhere between the eighth and fifteenth day. If you feel doubtful, consult the owner of the stud dog. Very often a breeder will agree to board your bitch for a day or two, to ensure a satisfactory mating. Incidentally, it really is cheaper in the long run to use an approved stud dog, rather than the dog next door. Pet dogs are sometimes reluctant or difficult to mate, and if you have misjudged the correct day you may have missed your chance of having a litter for another six months. It is only fair to say, though, that if your bitch gets out on her own she will probably mate quite successfully with the most unsuitable dog that she meets. During mating, after the dog has mounted the bitch, the two may remain "tied" for a period of fifteen minutes or longer. This is quite usual, but equally there may be a satisfactory mating without a tie.

PREGNANCY

Bitches may be scanned for pregnancy on day '28' post mating. This may confirm pregnancy, but not the number of conceptuses.

Pregnancy in the bitch lasts sixty-three days, but there may be a variation of several days in either direction. The whelping table will enable you to see the approximate date at which the pups are due. Pups that are born more than one week premature have a greatly reduced chance of survival. Overdue pups are better equipped for life, but their increased size may make for difficulties at birth.

Whelping table

Served January	Due to whelp March	Served February	Due to whelp April	Served March	Due to whelp May	Served April	Due to whelp June	Served May	Due to whelp July	Served June	Due to whelp August	Served July	Due to whelp September	Served August	Due to whelp October	Served September	Due to whelp November	Served October	Due to whelp December	Served November	Due to whelp January	Served December	Due to whelp February
1	5	1	5	1	3	1	3	1	3	1	3	1	2	1	3	1	3	1	3	1	3	1	2
2	6	2	6	2	4	2	4	2	4	2	4	2	3	2	4	2	4	2	4	2	4	2	3
3	7	3	7	3	5	3	5	3	5	3	5	3	4	3	5	3	5	3	5	3	5	3	4
4	8	4	8	4	6	4	6	4	6	4	6	4	5	4	6	4	6	4	6	4	6	4	5
5	9	5	9	5	7	5	7	5	7	5	7	5	6	5	7	5	7	5	7	5	7	5	6
6	10	6	10	6	8	6	8	6	8	6	8	6	7	6	8	6	8	6	8	6	8	6	7
7	11	7	11	7	9	7	9	7	9	7	9	7	8	7	9	7	9	7	9	7	9	7	8
8	12	8	12	8	10	8	10	8	10	8	10	8	9	8	10	8	10	8	10	8	10	8	9
9	13	9	13	9	11	9	11	9	11	9	11	9	10	9	11	9	11	9	11	9	11	9	10
10	14	10	14	10	12	10	12	10	12	10	12	10	11	10	12	10	12	10	12	10	12	10	11
11	15	11	15	11	13	11	13	11	13	11	13	11	12	11	13	11	13	11	13	11	13	11	12
12	16	12	16	12	14	12	14	12	14	12	14	12	13	12	14	12	14	12	14	12	14	12	13
13	17	13	17	13	15	13	15	13	15	13	15	13	14	13	15	13	15	13	15	13	15	13	14
14	18	14	18	14	16	14	16	14	16	14	16	14	15	14	16	14	16	14	16	14	16	14	15
15	19	15	19	15	17	15	17	15	17	15	17	15	16	15	17	15	17	15	17	15	17	15	16
16	20	16	20	16	18	16	18	16	18	16	18	16	17	16	18	16	18	16	18	16	18	16	17
17	21	17	21	17	19	17	19	17	19	17	19	17	18	17	19	17	19	17	19	17	19	17	18
18	22	18	22	18	20	18	20	18	20	18	20	18	19	18	20	18	20	18	20	18	20	18	19
19	23	19	23	19	21	19	21	19	21	19	21	19	20	19	21	19	21	19	21	19	21	19	20
20	24	20	24	20	22	20	22	20	22	20	22	20	21	20	22	20	22	20	22	20	22	20	21
21	25	21	25	21	23	21	23	21	23	21	23	21	22	21	23	21	23	21	23	21	23	21	22
22	26	22	26	22	24	22	24	22	24	22	24	22	23	22	24	22	24	22	24	22	24	22	23
23	27	23	27	23	25	23	25	23	25	23	25	23	24	23	25	23	25	23	25	23	25	23	24
24	28	24	28	24	26	24	26	24	26	24	26	24	25	24	26	24	26	24	26	24	26	24	25
25	29	25	29	25	27	25	27	25	27	25	27	25	26	25	27	25	27	25	27	25	27	25	26
26	30	26	30	26	28	26	28	26	28	26	28	26	27	26	28	26	28	26	28	26	28	26	27
27	31	27	May 1	27	29	27	29	27	29	27	29	27	28	27	29	27	29	27	29	27	29	27	28
28	Apr 1	28	2	28	30	28	30	28	30	28	30	28	29	28	30	28	30	28	30	28	30	28	Mar 1
29	2	29	3	29	31	29	July 1	29	31	29	31	29	30	29	31	29	Dec 1	29	31	29	31	29	2
30	3			30	June 1	30	2	30	Aug 1	30	Sept 1	30	Oct 1	30	Nov 1	30	2	30	Jan 1	30	Feb 1	30	3
31	4			31	2			31	2			31	2	31	2			31	2			31	4

Recognition of pregnancy

In an overweight bitch, or one that is really muscular, pregnancy may be very difficult to detect. Three weeks after mating, a Veterinary Surgeon may be able to detect the presence of puppies in the abdomen, which at this time feel rather like golf balls. After this time the pups start to grow, and become surrounded by protective fluid, and they may be much less easy to detect. At six to seven weeks the enlargement of the abdomen becomes apparent and increases rapidly up to full term at nine weeks.

From about six to seven weeks the mammary or milk glands begin to swell, and there may often be milk present, or overflowing in the last week.

The presence of pups may be detected in the last week of pregnancy (when their bones have become sufficiently developed) by the use of X-ray, or ultra-sound scans, but this is, as a rule, only done if there is some doubt as to whether the bitch is actually in whelp, or is very overdue.

Bitch's uterus before mating   *Bitch's uterus with whelps at three weeks*

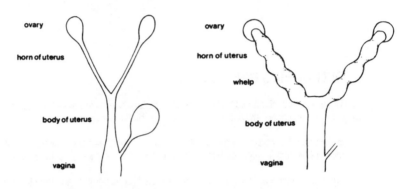

PREPARING FOR THE PUPS

It is important to decide in good time just where your bitch is going to have her pups. At this time, like people, they can become rather temperamental and she may be planning to have them on your eiderdown. Choose a quiet corner of the house, where she will not be disturbed, especially if there are children in the house, and get her used to sleeping there in the last weeks of pregnancy.

The bed and bedding

A suitable bed is a box, with sides of about eight inches high to prevent the pups rolling out. A railing or shelf a few inches away from each inside wall is a help to prevent the pups from being crushed when the mother turns round carelessly in the first few days.

The box should be in a situation free from draughts, as changes in temperature can be very harmful to new-born pups. A thick layer of clean newspaper is the ideal bedding material during whelping. A layer or two can be removed at a time, as it becomes soiled, without disturbing the bitch too much.

Whelping box showing drop front and protective shelf

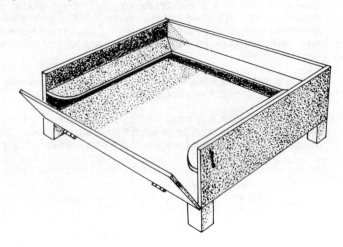

DIET DURING PREGNANCY

The in-whelp bitch should be fit, but not fat, so take care to increase the amount of food to be given rather cautiously, but be sure it is of high nutritional value.

In the first three weeks the growth of the pups are comparatively slow (indeed at this stage you may not be certain that your bitch is in pup), so it is wise to keep her on a normal balanced diet.

From four to nine weeks the growth of the pups is considerable, and the bitch will require a higher food intake, especially of protein, if she is not to lose condition. Proprietary dog foods are the best as they are carefully balanced.

Vitamin and mineral supplement

A dog receiving the suggested diet will be getting an adequate supply of vitamins, but for the bitch which is in poor condition, one that is reluctant to eat, or a "fussy" eater, a vitamin supplement such as Sherley's Vionate may be necessary. Consult your own Veterinary Surgeon for advice.

Sherley's Lactol can also be given to the bitch at this stage as an easily digested source of protein and an additional supply of calcium for the developing pups. You will probably find that your bitch becomes extremely hungry as the pregnancy progresses so it is best to divide the meals and feed three times daily. Where there is a large number of pups present the bitch may become less willing to eat in the later stages of pregnancy because of the abdominal discomfort, so it is wise to give small but frequent meals.

Laxatives

It is as well to see that the bitch is free from constipation in the later stages of pregnancy and a mild laxative prescribed by your Veterinary Surgeon may be given.

Exercise

Normal exercise should be continued through-out pregnancy until the bitch becomes too heavy to consider the daily walk a pleasure. Boisterous games, or running for a ball should be discouraged.

Bathing

If you normally bath your dog fairly frequently, it is safe to continue in pregnancy, but if there is to be any struggling it is better to dust a little baby's talcum powder into the coat, and then brush it over thoroughly to freshen up your pet. Sherley's Dry Revive is a very pleasant alternative. This is a refreshing liquid which can be rubbed into the coat, with no need to use water. For long-haired dogs such as pekes or poodles it may be helpful if the hair is trimmed from under the tail, and round the milk glands, to avoid soiling.

TREATMENT FOR WORMS

It is important to treat your bitch for roundworms at regular intervals of 3-6 months, but it is especially important after whelping and during the period when she is producing milk (see chapter 5 - Internal Parasites).

In the adult dog few roundworms are found in the gut, but their larvae remain as cysts in the muscles. During pregnancy, the larvae in these cysts break out and migrate through the bitch to the uterus where they infect the pups. Thus, the majority of pups are born with an established worm infection, and this is the reason why pups need to be wormed from a very early age.

Migrating larvae can also pass through the milk and act as another route of infection for the pups at this time. Additionally, the bitch can become re-infected from her pups whilst nursing, and it is therefore essential that she too be wormed every two weeks whilst she's feeding her pups.

PLANNING FOR THE BIRTH

Before the actual birth commences, it is a good idea to check that you have the following things in the house:
a) Soap, disinfectant, and a small hand basin. Hygiene is of first importance when handling the mother or pups.
b) Cotton wool for cleaning the pups' noses and mouths.
c) Several old small towels for drying the pups if necessary.
d) A pair of scissors, sterilised by boiling.
e) Some thick silk or cotton (boiled) to tie off the umbilical cords if necessary.
f) A cardboard box, containing a blanket, and a well wrapped hot water bottle, where the first pups may be placed if the bitch becomes upset and restless as other pups arrive.
g) Plenty of clean newspaper.

BEHAVIOUR AT WHELPING TIME

First stage of labour

In some instances the first stage of labour may be missed altogether, and you may come down to find that a litter of pups has arrived with very little warning. However, if you suspect that the pups are on the way it is wise to stay up, or to come down from time to time to check that all is well. It is a good idea to let your Veterinary Surgeon know in advance the date of the expected whelping, in case you need to call for his aid at some antisocial hour.

Very often the first stage lasts twenty-four hours, or even longer in the maiden bitch. There is usually marked restlessness, panting and sometimes crying, and the bitch will scratch up her bedding a great deal, imitating the behaviour of the primitive dog making a nest for its young. She will generally refuse food, and the temperature if checked will be found to have fallen from the normal of 101.5° F to 98° F. There is usually a rather clear, or mucous-like, discharge from the vulva, and the bitch will probably start to lick and clean herself a great deal.

Second stage of labour

Normally after the period of restlessness of the first stage of labour the bitch will go into the second stage of labour, in which contractions take place, as the bitch strains to expel the puppy. If these contractions do not follow after a reasonable time, or if the bitch appears to settle down again, it is wise to call a Veterinary Surgeon. It may be due to a condition know as primary uterine inertia, and an injection may be needed to accelerate the birth process.

At this time there will be more discharge and sometimes the appearance of the water bag, a membrane filled with fluid, at the vulva. This is the protective sac in which the puppy has developed inside the mother. If the bitch continues to strain vigorously for longer than thirty minutes without managing to expel the pup, it is wise to call for professional help, as there may be some abnormality. With a first litter the arrival of the first pup may cause considerable distress, but the later births may be comparatively easy.

NORMAL BIRTH

In the canine species the young are born in almost equal numbers, head first (which is usually considered as normal presentation) and hind feet first (or breech). The pup may be born still in its protective sac, but more commonly the sac will rupture, liberating a certain amount of clear fluid and the pup will be seen to be attached to its mother by the umbilical cord. This cord is attached to the placenta or afterbirth and this may be expelled with the pup (the third stage of labour).

Normal position of the pup at birth

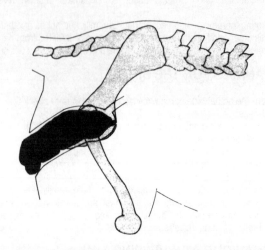

The new-born pup

The mother will then start to lick vigorously at the puppy, thus stimulating his breathing, and you will hear him gasp, or perhaps give his first indignant cry at her rough treatment. The mother will then, as a rule, bite at the umbilical cord to sever it (there is rarely much bleeding) and she will then eat the afterbirth. This may look revolting, but dogs have always done so, and there is a theory that there may be hormones in the membranes which are of value to the bitch. The placenta and foetal membranes of the bitch are normally dark-green in colour, and the bitch will tend to have a greenish or blood-stained discharge for some days after the birth of the pups. If the pup is strong and healthy he will almost at once make his way to the milk glands and start feeding. If the birth is proceeding normally, it is best to leave the bitch undisturbed as far as possible, but the owner should stay near at hand in case of difficulties. A puppy may easily be lost for lack of a little assistance at the right moment.

With the first litter, the bitch may at first appear rather mystified, or even frightened of the first pup. It is important then to immediately break the sac, if the pup is still in it, either with the fingers or with sterilised scissors, open the mouth and start the pup breathing, and rub it fairly vigorously with a soft, dry towel.

Cutting the cord

If the pup is still attached to the placenta (or the mother) by its umbilical cord this must be cut. First tie off the cord firmly at about two inches away from the pup, taking care not to pull at the stomach wall, then cut through on the side of the knot away from the puppy using sterilised scissors. As soon as possible put the pup back with its mother, talking to her soothingly until she accepts it.

Removing the pup from its protective sac   *Tying and cutting the umbilical cord*

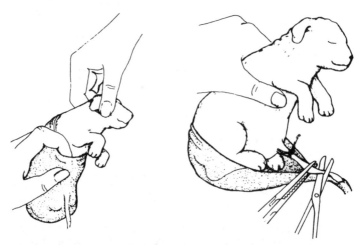

After the arrival of the first pup the bitch may feel very tired and settle down for a sleep. Usually after a period varying from twenty minutes to an hour or more, contractions will start again, and the rest of the pups will be born at various intervals. If longer than three hours elapses without any straining it is best to consult a Veterinary Surgeon. Particularly in older dogs the muscle of the uterus (womb) becomes fatigued, and again an injection may be necessary. This is called secondary uterine inertia.

Counting the afterbirths

Sometimes the afterbirth is not expelled at the same time as the puppy, and may be shed with or after the next pup. It is important to check that one afterbirth has arrived with each puppy, because if one is retained it can lead to serious illness in the bitch. If the bitch does not at once take to her pups, or if she becomes restless and inclined to tread on them when contractions start again, they should be placed in a box in a warm spot, with a well protected hot water bottle. They will soon stop crying and snuggle up to the heat.

REVIVAL OF PUPS

Even if a puppy at birth looks blue, cold or dead, it may still be capable of revival. Immediately place it in a warm spot (at about 80°F). Open its mouth and pull the tongue out gently and blow into the mouth, in the manner of mouth to mouth resuscitation. It is not necessary (or desirable) for you to place your mouth over the pups mouth for this method to be successful. The pup should be held with its head slightly down to encourage any fluid drainage from its lungs. Continue rubbing all over gently with a pad of cotton wool, or a soft towel. If any breathing is seen it is well worth persevering. Pups have been known to recover even after an hour of apparent death.

NORMAL AND ABNORMAL PRESENTATIONS

If the puppy is arriving in either of the two normal presentations or positions (that is head or breech), but the bitch is having difficulty in expelling it completely, the owner may attempt to help. Grip the pup carefully with a clean dry towel, rotate it slightly from side to side and then as the bitch strains, pull steadily with a downward action.

Dystokia is the name applied to difficult or abnormal birth. In simple cases it may be possible for an owner to give assistance, but an unqualified person should never attempt an internal manipulation and the use of whelping forceps in inexperienced hands can be very dangerous indeed.

When to send for help

If after the bitch has strained for some time only one foot appears at the vulva it suggests that the pup is in an abnormal or transverse position, and the owner should not, on any account, attempt to remove the puppy. Get in touch with a Veterinary Surgeon at once, as any delay may risk the life not only of the pups, but of the mother as well. In an emergency the only helpful action is to attempt to push the pup back beyond the neck of the womb, in the hope that the puppy may turn itself into a more satisfactory position.

CARE OF THE BITCH AFTER WHELPING

It may be difficult for an owner to be certain whether or not a bitch has finished whelping. As a rule, after producing the last pup (and afterbirth) she will stop panting and shivering, clean herself and her pups, and settle down contentedly to feed her family. If she can be persuaded to go out to relieve herself at this point, it will give you the opportunity to remove the soiled bedding, and to check that the pups are sound and healthy.

If you are uncertain whether or not your bitch has finished whelping, it is always best to consult a Veterinary Surgeon. It has been known for a bitch to produce a live pup after an interval of twenty-four hours, but if a dead puppy is retained the bitch will soon become seriously ill.

Discharges

There will normally be a blood-stained discharge for at least a week after arrival of the pups, and this will gradually become clear, and dry up altogether. A persistent, or foul smelling discharge is a danger signal, and may indicate the presence of a dead pup, or a retained afterbirth. Get advice at once.

Remember that puppies are normally born with their eyes closed, and do not open them until about the tenth to fourteenth day.

Abnormal pups

Occasionally, deformed puppies are born with abnormalities varying from cleft palate, to the absence of a limb, to the complete absence of the stomach wall. The pups should be removed without the bitch seeing if possible, and painlessly destroyed by a Veterinary Surgeon.

TROUBLE AFFECTING THE MILK GLANDS

An excess of milk may cause the bitch to become uncomfortable and restless, and she may refuse to let the pups feed. This can be relieved by squeezing the teat to draw off a little of the milk and reduce the pressure.

The sharp claws of the pups may sometimes make painful scratches on the teats, and in this case it helps to trim the points of the claws with scissors.

Mastitis

A very hard red swollen teat may indicate mastitis or infection in the milk gland. It is important to get veterinary help as soon as possible as the contaminated milk can cause the death of the pups.

MILK FEVER OR ECLAMPSIA

This is a very serious condition and it may be very sudden in onset. It results from a shortage of calcium in the blood stream, and it is usually seen in bitches in poor condition which have had large litters, though it may occur unexpectedly in bitches which are plump and well.

Symptoms

The bitch may appear drowsy or unsteady on her legs. There is often twitching of the muscles and if no treatment is given convulsions follow. An injection of calcium will usually produce an immediate improvement, so seek veterinary attention at once.

FEEDING DURING LACTATION

During the actual whelping the bitch may be offered small drinks of water and glucose, but once the family is complete she will probably feel hungry and appreciate a bowl of meat broth, or beaten egg and milk. The nutritional requirements of the bitch while feeding her pups are very high indeed, and she can be fed more or less to her capacity, having meals every four hours. Even bitches which do not normally like milk will usually take it at this time so Lactol, milk puddings, and cereals can be alternated with her normal diet. It is wise to add a vitamin and mineral supplement to the diet. When the pups are being weaned, the amount of food given to the bitch can be gradually reduced.

Water

A lack of fluid in the diet will quickly reduce the supply of milk, so see that fresh water is always available.

REARING AND FEEDING THE PUPS

In the first three weeks of life a good mother will care for her pups totally. She will not only feed and clean them, but by her constant licking help to ensure that both bladder and bowels are functioning.

At three to four weeks it is wise to start a gradual weaning process to avoid putting too much strain on the mother, especially if there is a large litter. Proprietary foods, especially formulated for young puppies, are available from your pet shop. If the pup is not keen to start solid food, soak it in some freshly prepared Lactol first. Put the food on a flattish plate, or dish, and encourage the pups to feed by dipping your finger in the mixture and smearing a little around their mouths. Try to give three meals daily, while the pups are still feeding from the mother as well, and be patient; pups can be exasperatingly clumsy when they first start to feed.

Feed each puppy separately to ensure fair shares and prevent a weak pup from being pushed out.

Six weeks

By six weeks the pups should be taking four meals daily, and taking very little food from the mother (who will probably be beginning to get tired of them). Fresh water should be available in a heavy flat container that will not tip over easily, or drown an adventurous pup.

By this time the pups will be cutting their first teeth, so you can start to introduce dog biscuits. A large strong home-made rag doll will also give them exercise, and keep them out of mischief, whilst having a lot of fun.

Puppy care

Pups should never be sent to their new homes until they are completely weaned and independent of the mother if they are to have a fair chance to grow and thrive.

Fleas and lice

Young pups can easily become infected with fleas and lice, and apart from the obvious irritation and discomfort which they cause, they may result in a considerable deterioration in health and condition. For a purchaser to find that the new puppy is "lousy" is usually a great shock and reflects badly on the reputation of the breeder. The answer is simple; always examine your pups thoroughly once each week (grooming with a flea comb is a good idea). If you find any parasites, consult your Veterinary Surgeon for a suitable treatment that can safely be used on young puppies.

Worming

Roundworms can make tiny puppies really ill. The symptoms are usually poor growth, lack of appetite and swollen stomachs.

Treatment can be given safely with one of Sherley's worming preparations, even from as young as two weeks, and will need to be repeated every two weeks until weaning (see Chapter 5 – Internal Parasites).

THE BITCH AT WEANING

Sometimes at weaning a bitch will start to vomit her food. This is probably a reversion to primitive times when the wild dog would regurgitate its half digested food to feed its pups. It can usually be cured by feeding the bitch in a room well away from the sight and sound of her pups.

If, when the pups are completely weaned, the bitch still continues to make a lot of milk, you should ask your Veterinary Surgeon for help with the problem.

ACCOMMODATION FOR THE PUPS

A play area

For the first three weeks the pups will usually be content to stay in the box with their mother, but after that they will start to become adventurous. Try to close off a corner of the room to give the pups an area to play safely without risk of being stepped on. A baby's old play pen is ideal, but you can improvise with fire screens, or old boxes.

Put a tray of sand or litter in a corner, and start to toilet train the pups by putting them there after each feed. Sherley's Swiftie Puppy Trainer will help this process.

As the pups become larger, and more boisterous, it is important also to give the mother the opportunity to get away from them for a little peace!

REARING ORPHAN PUPS

Keeping warm

If you are left with a litter of orphan pups to rear, it is well worth trying to find a foster mother. The mother dog puts in hours of patient work to keep her pups clean, warm and well fed, so if you are to be the substitute be prepared for some very hard work. Warmth is essential to young pups. The room should be maintained at 80°F, and it is wise to get a thermometer, rather than trust in your own judgement.

In addition there should be a hot water bottle, well wrapped in a woolly cover and kept at a constant temperature, placed in the box itself. The pups will snuggle up to this, and to each other and sleep contentedly. The box itself should have high sides to prevent the pups climbing out. Put a warm cover (such as part of an old dressing gown) at the sleeping end of the box, and cover the floor with a thick layer of newspaper, which can easily be changed when it is soiled. A lamp of the kind used for rearing baby pigs can be useful to maintain an even heat in the box.

Lactol

Lactol can be used as a complete food for the first three weeks, in substitution for the bitch's milk (given according to the instructions). At first the pups should be fed every two to three hours, but as they start to take more food at a time the intervals can become longer.

An eye dropper can be used as a feeder in an emergency, but a premature baby pipette is usually the most successful method. Make sure that the opening in the teat is large enough to allow the milk to flow easily.

Hygiene

Hygiene is of the greatest importance. The orphan pup which has not received the colostrums, or first milk, from the mother is more susceptible to infections.

After each meal the pups should be wiped over with a piece of damp clean cotton wool round the face and paws to remove stale food. The stomach should be massaged with a pad of cotton wool to stimulate the action of the bladder and bowels (in imitation of the licking of the mother), and after cleaning with damp gauze or cotton wool the pup should be thoroughly dried.

If puppies develop either constipation or diarrhoea, it is best to seek Veterinary advice.

Weaning

Orphans pups can usually be weaned quite early, using one of the strained baby foods at first, and their diet can then continue as for normal pups.

DEW-CLAWS AND DOCKING

Many dogs live quite happily with dewclaws (the vestigial "thumbs" of the dog), but if they become caught and tear, they can be very painful. Dew-claws can easily be removed by a Veterinary Surgeon.

It is still possible to dock some dogs (i.e. surgically remove most of the tail), but it is now illegal to do it yourself, and most Veterinary Surgeons will only do it if there is a medical reason.

After all, dogs were designed with tails.

REGISTERING PEDIGREE PUPS

If you are selling your pedigree pups, it is best to register them with the Kennel Club before sale. You must supply the new owner with a completed pedigree form showing the parentage. These forms can usually be obtained from pet shops and it is a good idea to get them and make them out well before you advertise your pups for sale. Sherley's will also supply suitable pedigree forms direct on request. The new owner will then have to register the puppy themselves, using a "Change of Ownership" form.

CARING FOR YOUR PUPPY

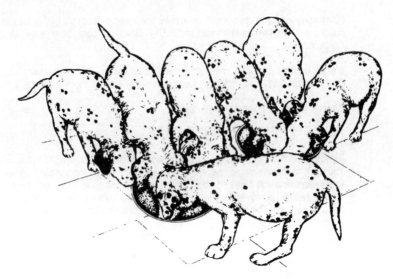

The new puppy

The arrival of a new puppy in the home is always an exciting event, especially for children. Remember, though, that the pup will be feeling strange and should be allowed to settle in quietly without too much picking up, or fussing.

A CORNER OF HIS OWN

Bed or basket

It is important that the new pet should have his own bed or basket in a quiet, draught-free corner of the room, right from the start. This is his own territory and it will help to give him a sense of security in his new home. Start at once to teach him the command "into your basket" and see that it is obeyed.

Warm and cosy

A strong cardboard box, with one side cut down, will make a warm and satisfactory first bed, with a piece of old blanket, or synthetic washable sheepskin for bedding. A fairly thick layer of newspaper at the bottom of the box will give warmth and insulation and it can be discarded daily.

Place the basket near a radiator if possible, as young pups feel the cold, or supply an old stone hot water bottle, well wrapped up.

It has been suggested that a clock with a loud tick placed near the basket may sound to the puppy like the heart beat of its mother, and provide a little reassurance.

LEAVING YOUR PUP

At night

A puppy which has just left his litter of brothers and sisters, and finds himself alone at night for the first time, may well feel lonely and howl. If you are certain that he is not hungry or cold, ignore the noise if you possibly can, although if there are neighbours to consider it is difficult. If you can harden your heart for a few nights, the puppy really will get tired of barking, but if you once weaken and take him into the bedroom or worse still, the bed, the battle is lost.

It really is not a kindness to make your pup over dependent on you. A dog which sleeps in its own basket and feels secure there can much more easily be left with friends, or in kennels if it ever becomes necessary.

Going shopping

For the same reason, it is wise to make a point of leaving your pup alone in the house for a short time each day (while you go shopping for instance). In this way he will accept being left as the normal thing, and feel confident that you will return.

SIMPLE TRAINING

It is no use expecting too much of a young pup in the way of training, but house training, and a few simple commands should be taught, and persevered with.

If you are lucky, your pup may have had some house training before his arrival in the home, but if not, prepare to be patient.

House training

Training to newspaper is usually the best method, unless the garden is very close to the kitchen and the weather is good. In any case, newspapers will be needed at night as the young puppy cannot be expected to be clean over a period of hours. Put several thicknesses of newspaper on the floor near the puppy's basket, and put the puppy onto it immediately after feeding, as soon as he wakes up, and indeed on every occasion when you think it may be necessary. Praise him when he uses the paper; most pups are anxious to please.

Day and night

If the puppy does not at once take to the idea of using the newspapers, a few drops of Sherley's Swiftie Puppy Trainer sprinkled on the paper will often give him the idea that this is the right place. On the other hand, it is important to disinfect thoroughly if the puppy happens to soil the carpets, as dogs tend to return by scent to the same place. Stain removers are available from pet shops to remove soil marks made on soft furnishings. It is better at this stage to confine the puppy entirely to the kitchen, where there is an easily washable floor, until clean habits have been established. It is well worth devoting a lot of time to this early training. A puppy which has once learned dirty habits in the house can be very difficult to retrain. As the puppy gets older, and has more bladder and bowel control, start training him to the garden or yard, but remember that you will probably have to continue with newspapers at night for some time.

Commands

Keep commands simple at this stage. The pup should learn to go into his box, or basket, and "stay" when told. Be consistent with your commands, even when you are busy, and see that they are obeyed. Teach the pup to come when his name is called, and of course make a fuss of him when he does so. A pup which will not come when he is called is not only a nuisance to his owner, but may be in real danger if he gets loose in traffic.

Calling him by name each meal time will help to teach obedience and associate coming to the call with something pleasant.

Collar and lead

Start early to let your pup wear his collar for a short time each day. Some pups resent a collar at first and sulk, but this is an important lesson and you must persevere. A medallion with your name and address is a "must" as even young pups sometimes stray. Alternatively, a Sherley's Lost & Found Collar will help identify your puppy, and can be used from 12 weeks of age.

Whether you prefer a collar or a harness, get your pup used to walking on the lead in the house or garden. Nothing looks worse than an unfortunate pup being dragged along the streets by his collar, because he has not been taught to walk properly.

Enrol your puppy at a training school as soon as possible. You will both have a lot of fun, and a well-trained dog is both a more pleasant companion and less trouble to other people.

FEEDING THE PUPPY

The main ingredients of a puppy's diet are milk, meat in some form to supply protein, and biscuits or cereal to supply carbohydrates. Complete puppy foods make life simple, as they are especially designed for growing pups.

Milk

Milk supplies Calcium and Vitamin D, which are essential for bone formation. Sherley's Lactol is specially formulated to take the place of the bitch's own milk. It is greatly superior to cow's milk, as it is formulated to match bitch's milk as closely as possible. It is therefore more suitable for puppies than other preparations. It is also ideal for pregnant and nursing bitches.

Food needs

With puppies there is little danger of overfeeding. Their dietary requirements are very much greater than those of adult dogs, in proportion to their weight. The main growing period in a dog's life is between seven weeks and six months, so it is vital that at this time your puppy is given the right foods in the right amounts. Neglect, or wrong feeding can lead to poor bone formation, bad teeth, or stunted growth.

It is possible that your puppy will arrive with a diet sheet prepared by his breeder. If this appears to be suiting him, by all means continue with it. If, however, you need to make changes, do so gradually as young pups, like babies, are easily upset by sudden changes of food.

Age seven to twelve weeks. At this stage pups should have four small meals per day, reducing to three meals daily towards the end of this period if wished.

Type of food

Most well known manufacturers now produce ready prepared, complete diets (either tinned, moist, or dry) which are specially formulated for young puppies. These are to be recommended as they take all the guess work and worry out of preparing your own diets. Follow the manufacturers advice for the amounts required.

For puppies, as for adult dogs, fresh water should always be available.

Age twelve weeks to six months. Three meals daily are usually sufficient, increasing the quantities as the puppy grows. Usually the first meal or breakfast is the milky one and the other two are of meat and biscuit. If the pup seems to get tired of cereals and milk just give a drink of milk with a rusk or hard biscuit in the morning.

Age six months to one year. Two meals daily should be the practice. These may be morning and evening, or mid-day and evening, according to the dog's appetite, or to suit the owner's way of life. By this age both meals are of meat and biscuit, but by all means continue with a small drink of milk daily, if your dog enjoys it.

QUANTITIES TO FEED

This is a very difficult subject to generalise on, as puppies of the different breeds obviously vary greatly in size. As a guideline, a puppy which is being fed four times daily can be given as much food as it will clear up straight away at each meal time, but also follow the manufacturer's advice as to quantity.

Regular routine

If your puppy is well and active, and food is being left, you are almost certainly overfeeding. If, however, your puppy is not taking its food, and seems quiet and listless, you would be wise to consult your Veterinary Surgeon. Try to keep regular meal times. A pup has a small stomach capacity and will thrive much better on frequent small meals rather than on one large one. If any food is left, don't leave it on the floor to harbour germs, but take it up straight away.

Vitamin and mineral supplements may be needed for a pup which is in poor condition. However, care must be taken not to give excessive amounts of certain vitamins and minerals, e.g. Vitamin D

and Calcium, as they may cause more harm than good.
Suitable balanced formulations exist. e.g. Sherley's Vionate, but if you are unsure consult your Veterinary Surgeon who will advise you about requirements and dose.

TEETHING

Your pup will have a complete set of sharp puppy teeth when he arrives – as you will probably soon find out!

Puppy teeth
Between the ages of twelve weeks and six months he will gradually shed his puppy teeth, and cut his permanent, or adult teeth. The first permanent teeth to come through are usually the two centre teeth on the top jaw, and the last are the big corner or canine teeth in the top and bottom jaw. Most puppies change their teeth with very little discomfort, but occasionally there may be some soreness or bleeding.

In a few cases, and more often in miniature breeds, the puppy's teeth are not shed before the permanent teeth start to come through. This not only causes discomfort to the pup, but may spoil the shape of the mouth so if this occurs it is best to consult a Veterinary Surgeon.

Chewing
While the teething process is going on, pups tend to chew everything so learn to be tidy. Never leave shoes, or indeed anything chewable, within the puppy's reach – and don't give the pup an old shoe as a plaything. He cannot be expected to distinguish the old from the new. Dental chews are now available for dogs of all ages, and these will not only deter your puppy from chewing your personal belongings, but will also help to keep his teeth clean and healthy.

GROOMING AND BATHING

Puppies don't usually need to be bathed, but if it should be necessary use lukewarm water and a mild dog shampoo and take care to see that the puppy is thoroughly dried and not allowed to become chilled. Sherley's Puppy Shampoo is ideal for this. It is a mild, conditioning shampoo, especially formulated for sensitive young skins.

Brushing
Brushing and combing should be carried out daily, especially with the long coated varieties. It is never too soon to start good habits. A fairly soft nylon brush is often best at this stage.

Fleas
Puppies, even from the best of homes, may sometimes have fleas. There is no need to be unduly alarmed about this, as these fleas do not live on humans. Fleas on young puppies should be removed using a flea comb. Bathing in a puppy shampoo may also remove a great many of the fleas. Powder and sprays should not be used on puppies younger than 12 weeks of age. Bedding should be regularly washed, and treated with Sherley's Defest II to prevent reinfestation of the puppies (see also our leaflet on flea control).

YOUR PUPPY'S HEALTH

Vaccination
Vaccination against the major infectious diseases of dogs is the most important step you should take to guarantee your pup's health.

Vaccination will give you protection against the following diseases:

Distemper – An often fatal viral disease in unprotected dogs.
Adenovirus – This causes a viral hepatitis and can also cause respiratory disease.
Parainfluenza – A viral respiratory disease.
Parvovirus – A viral infection causing severe diarrhoea and sickness which can be fatal.
Leptospira – Two types of this bacteria exist; one causing a severe hepatitis, the other causing a severe kidney disease. Protection against both forms is included in the vaccination.

NEVER put off vaccination, it could cost your pet it's life!

Isolation

Puppies should be kept in their own homes prior to vaccination, and isolated from contact with other unvaccinated dogs to prevent infection. Viral diseases are extremely infectious, and may be picked up from the ground, even without actual contact with another dog. Any grass verge, where other dogs are walked, can be a potential source of infection.

Age for vaccination

The vaccination course is usually started between eight and twelve weeks of age. It is best to get in touch with your local Veterinary Surgeon to make arrangements as soon as you get your new puppy.

Most pups have some roundworms, even though they may have come from a good home and have had some previous treatment.

Worming

It is a good idea to dose the puppy routinely at regular intervals with, for example, Sherley's Worming Syrup, in his early life, both for his sake, and to avoid any risk of infection to children. Worms may cause illness in young pups, but if your pup is listless or off his food, don't conclude that this is the cause, without consulting a Veterinary Surgeon.

A healthy puppy

A healthy puppy should be ready for its meals, and clear them up at once. It should have a shiny coat, and bright eyes, and be plump, without being overweight. It should be lively and alert and ready to play. If your puppy answers to this description, you have got off to a good start.

CARING FOR YOUR DOG

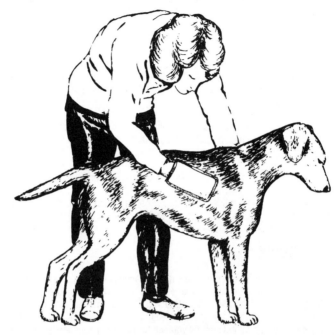

Adult dogs and problem dogs

Taking on an adult dog as a pet may be something of a gamble. He may have been well brought up and be thoroughly obedient, in which case you will have avoided all the work and trouble of house-training and discipline. On the other hand, he may have been allowed to run wild and you will have a very difficult task ahead to train him into your ways. It may happen that out of kindness, you inherit a pet from a friend or relative who cannot keep it, and if it is no longer young you will probably have to accept, and live with, its faults. However, if you plan to buy an adult dog, or answer an advertisement for one wanting a good home, do try to find out why the last owner is parting with it. It may turn out to chase motorcycles, bite people or kill chickens. Do not take on someone else's problems unless you are really used to dogs, and feel able to deal with them. It is no kindness to the problem dog if he is to be passed from one home to another. There are many good training schools around the country. Look in your local newspaper or Yellow Pages, or ask your local pet shop. Alternatively, contact the Association of Pet Dog Trainers (details on page 93).

HIS OWN CORNER IN THE HOUSE

Discipline

The adult dog, like a pup, should always have his own box, or basket, placed in a quiet draught-free corner of the room and he should learn from the start to go into his basket, and stay there when told. Do not let your dog sit on the chairs, or if you must, then see that he has one old chair that is his own. You may not mind having your clothes covered in dogs' hair, but it can be very hard on unsuspecting visitors.

WHAT KIND OF BED?

Now that your dog has, we hope, passed the stage of chewing things, it is time to choose a suitable bed. You may decide on the traditional basket, but a strong wooden box, with one side

Clean bedding

cut down, is equally good. In either case the bed should be large enough for the dog to stretch out comfortably and should be provided with a thick piece of blanket as a mattress. It is worth remembering that the eggs of fleas are shed in the bedding so see that the dog blankets are washed regularly. Canvas beds, on metal frames, are comfortable and easy to clean, and they fold away for travelling. Plastic is used both to make a basket type bed, or to cover a padded metal frame, to make a more comfortable and draught-free bed.

KENNELS

If your dog is to live in a kennel make sure that it is warm and weather-proof. It should be constructed of wood, and should be raised off the ground to avoid damp and draughts. Except in very good weather, it is preferable that the kennel should be placed inside another building, such as a garage or shed.

If the kennel is to serve as a permanent home for the dog it should be large enough to contain a raised bench type bed, and should stand in its own concrete run, in some part of the garden protected from cold winds or hot sun.

Straw may be used as bedding and it is best burned after use.

Disinfection

Faeces should be removed from the kennel daily to avoid build up of worm infestations and the whole floor area swilled out with disinfectant. The benches should be scrubbed with disinfectant at least weekly. Sherley's recommend Beaclean Dog Disinfectant for this purpose.

EXERCISE

Walks and runs

Adequate exercise is of the greatest importance in keeping a dog happy and healthy. "Adequate exercise" means at least one hour daily, for all except the toy breeds, and more if possible. Let it be a good run off the lead, not a dreary trail round streets, or worse still, shops. If you find this impossible to manage, a good game with a ball will help to tire out the dog without tiring its owner too much. If you cannot commit yourself to exercising your dog properly, you must ask yourself if you really should have a dog.

TRAINING

Exercising your dog will only be a pleasure if he has learned at least the rudiments of discipline and training. If you have brought your dog up from a puppy, the training programme should be fairly easy. He should have learned the one important lesson that when you give an order you really mean it. Half-hearted commands leave the dog feeling uncertain and, like children, they are inclined to get away with as much as they can. With a dog of six months or over behaviour patterns have been built up, and training is much more difficult, and requires endless patience.

WALKING ON THE LEAD

It is only too common to see dog owners being dragged around the streets by their dogs, making passers-by wonder who is taking whom for a walk.

A puppy can be accustomed to walking with a collar and lead from a very early age. It is best to start with a narrow, soft collar at first, and let him wear it constantly until he gets used to it. You can then attach a light lead and gradually coax him to walk along with you. If he lags behind or runs ahead, a few short, gentle tugs are all that should ever be used. Try to stay together, so the pup won't feel the lead too much and won't start to think of it as an uncomfortable restraint.

Pulling on the lead

With an older dog who has got into the habit of pulling, you will need to be more severe. If necessary, use a choke chain type of collar to help you control him. Speak to him very sharply, and pull him back to the level of your legs each time that he pulls. When your dog has become used to walking quite nicely on the lead, try teaching him to walk "at heel" off the lead. Choose a quiet place for this lesson, away from distractions and, of course, away from traffic. Make him halt and sit at road crossings, and never cross until he gets the word of command.

In some cases, special training collars available from pet shops or Veterinary Surgeons can be very useful for the dog that insists on pulling on the lead despite all efforts to prevent it.

Traffic

It is not wise to allow even a well-trained dog to walk off the lead on a road where there is busy traffic. A sudden distraction, such as a dog on the other side of the road, may cause him to forget his training with fatal results.

Cleanliness

If you live in a town, never allow your dog to foul the pavement. Walk him along the outside of the pavement, and step out into the gutter as soon as you think that he is about to defecate, taking care to see that he is not so far out in the road as to be in danger from passing cars. Councils now insist that owners are responsible for removing dog faeces from public areas and so you should always carry one of the many "poop-scoops" when taking your dog for a walk in a public place. Plastic bags can also be used to clear up after your dogs, and these should be disposed of in the bins provided or taken home to dispose of in the domestic waste.

Finally, and it should not be necessary to say, never turn your dog out to take a run on his own, even though you may feel that you live in a quiet situation. This not only shows a callous disregard for your dog's welfare, but may be the cause of a serious accident.

'Come'

Every dog should learn to come when called by name, or to a whistle, otherwise exercising off the lead becomes a hazard and a danger.

Start training in a confined space, in the house or garden. Call your dog to you in an encouraging tone of voice and make a great fuss of him when he comes. Do this three or four times each day, but do not continue too long or he will become bored.

If he is slow to learn this lesson an extending lead or even a length of clothes line will be useful to pull him sharply towards you as you call and then, of course, praise him when he comes. With older dogs that have not learned to come to a call it may be necessary to use a piece of cheese or meat as reward, but it is better not to start this system if it can be avoided.

Never chase after your dog, or puppy, if he runs away. This soon becomes a game to him, and you will find that he can run much faster than you. If you are outside, call him in an encouraging tone of voice, bending or kneeling on the ground, and holding your arms out. In an emergency it is sometimes effective to call your dog while running in the opposite direction, to distract him from crossing a busy road, or some other danger. Finally, however exasperated you may be feeling, do not scold your dog when he finally does come back. He will only be more reluctant to return next time.

'Sit' and 'stay'

Teach your dog to "sit" by pressing him firmly down on the hindquarters, while repeating the command in a fairly stern voice. When this lesson has been thoroughly mastered, tell him to "sit" then "stay" while you walk a few paces away. If he attempts to follow you speak to him sternly, and put him back in his place. Gradually increase the distance and then try moving just out of his sight, preferably in such a way that you can still see him and call out "stay" if he starts to move.

Make your dog sit while you prepare his meal every day, then wait until he hears the command to come.

Regular teeth cleaning means that your dog will be used to you examining his mouth. This is very helpful when giving medicine, etc. so that he does not resent handling.

GOOD MANNERS IN THE HOUSE

If your dog is to be a pleasure to you he must learn "polite manners" in the house. He will, of course, by now have learned to be clean in the house. Nervous puppies may still sometimes urinate if there is some excitement, or if a visitor calls, but this is fairly normal, and is a habit that they will soon grow out of. It is better not to rebuke them sharply as this simply makes a timid puppy even more so.

Visitors

Your dog should also have learned to go into his own bed when told and stay there, not to commandeer the best chair in the house, with his feet covered in mud. You may want your puppy to learn to be a watch dog, but do train him to give a warning only when strangers approach, not to go on and on barking. Do not let your dog jump up to greet you, or your friends. This may sound harsh advice, but muddy paws or torn stockings are not pleasant. Bend down to stroke your dog, and speak to him firmly if he jumps up, saying "down" in a stern voice.

Adolescent dogs, when they become excited, will often attempt to mount strange dogs, or the legs of visitors. This rather embarrassing habit should be checked, saying "down" in a very firm voice, or by distracting the dog by spraying it with water from a plant spray or water pistol. Any discipline must be carried out immediately so that the dog associates this with its bad behaviour. Dogs are very quick to learn what is and what is not acceptable behaviour.

Never feed your dog at the table, you have only yourself to blame if he makes a nuisance of himself by begging at meal times. If you want to give him the scraps, put them into his own dish, and give them at the proper feeding time. And, of course, never start the bad habit of giving sweets to your dog. They are bad for his teeth and his figure – and we all know of dogs who spring to life when they hear a sweet paper rustle. Sweets are not a natural, or a necessary, item of your dog's diet, and if you do not start the bad habit, he will never miss them.

TEACHING TRICKS

Some dogs, such as Poodles, have a natural aptitude for learning tricks and seem to enjoy them, but as a general rule this is not something that should be encouraged.

Tricks such as begging, or walking on the hind legs may be positively harmful, especially in the long bodied type of dog. There is always the danger that they may overbalance, causing injury to the spine.

TRAINING CLASSES

All dogs will benefit from attending dog-training classes, which are held in many districts now. They are particularly helpful because they teach the owner how to train his or her own dog. One word of warning though. It is important to carry on with the training programme at home as well.

Some people send their dogs away to be trained. This can sometimes be successful, but only too often a dog which has worked well with a trainer comes home and immediately reverts to its previous bad behaviour. This probably points to the truth that there are bad owners, as well as bad dogs.

Specialised training

There are also specialised types of training classes for the different breeds. German Shepherd and Labrador societies organise obedience training classes, Labradors, Spaniels, Retrievers and other sporting breeds can attend field trials, and Bloodhounds can be taught tracking. All these are sensible ways of making the most of your dog's natural intelligence, and they can provide a satisfying hobby for the owner.

GROOMING AND ROUTINE DOG CARE

Grooming equipment

All dogs need regular grooming. It improves the appearance of short coated varieties and it is absolutely essential for those with long and curly coats. It also does much to minimise the amount of hair shed on furniture and carpets. Start as you mean to go on. If you get your puppy used to a daily grooming from an early age he will accept it as a normal routine, and as a rule, get to enjoy it.

For short-haired varieties a fairly firm close brush is usually best. It will remove the loose hair and give a shine to the coat. A rubber glove stroked firmly down the coat will also help to remove excess hair, especially in the moulting season, and a final polish with a soft duster will give a nice finish to the grooming.

For long-haired breeds, a slicker brush and long-bristled brush are essential. So many owners think that they are grooming their dog when they are actually only running a brush over the surface of the tangles. A daily grooming should prevent the formation of matts and tangles, even in Spaniels and Poodles, but if they have been allowed to form, it is best to cut them out with scissors. Use a blunt-ended pair of scissors, a good light, and care – and do not worry about the bare places, the hair will soon grow again. If you tug away at painful tangles your dog will soon dread the sight of the brush, and grooming will become an ordeal to be avoided.

Parasites

Remember while grooming your dog to look for parasites such as fleas and lice which may have been picked-up and to deal with them appropriately (see Chapter 5 dealing with External Parasites).

You may also find grass seeds in the coat, and especially between the toes. If not removed, these may penetrate the skin causing painful abscesses. A daily examination of the coat will also give you the opportunity to check for any signs of scurf or skin irritations that may need attention.

Foot care

The feet should be examined daily, especially in hairy types of dogs, such as Spaniels, for the presence of thorns. It is better to keep the hair between the toes and under the pads trimmed short, and to wash the feet after exercise in muddy weather. The accumulation of grit and hard packed mud under the pads may contribute to the formation of interdigital cysts or boils on the feet. These are most commonly seen in dogs which have deep "wells" under the toes, which collect mud. Regular care of the feet can do much to avoid this trouble. Sherley's recommend Beaphar Propolis Foot Balm to soothe sore, dry or cracked pads.

NAIL CUTTING

Dogs that live in the town usually get sufficient exercise on hard ground to keep their nails short, and indeed in some cases the nails may become worn too far down, with painful results. However, dogs living in the country or being exercised mainly on soft ground may require a manicure.

Dew-claws

It is important to remember that the nail of the dog has a very sensitive "quick" and it is only the hard, horny tip that is to be trimmed. Use a strong pair of nail cutters, and little and often is the best policy to follow. You will hurt your dog if you cut the nail too short, and there may well be considerable bleeding – and you must not be surprised if your dog is very apprehensive when a manicure is necessary again. The dew-claws should not be forgotten when trimming the nails. These extra claws, or thumbs, are situated on the inner aspect of the legs, sometimes on the front paws only, but sometimes on the back also. They are of no use to the civilised dog, and indeed they are often removed soon after birth. Because they do not wear at all, they may sometimes become ingrowing and cause the dog considerable distress before the cause of the trouble is realised. They are also inclined to become caught and broken if they are too long, leaving a painful exposed quick.

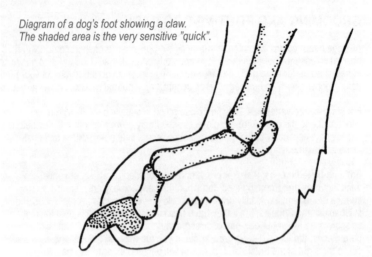

Diagram of a dog's foot showing a claw.
The shaded area is the very sensitive "quick".

BATHING

Lather and rinse

While regular grooming can do a great deal to keep a dog's coat looking clean and trim, from time to time a bath becomes necessary. White dogs which live in the town need fairly frequent bathing if they are not to become grey dogs, and dogs which have the unfortunate habit of rolling on anything disagreeable that they can find become frequent candidates for the tub. However, apart from this, any dog which lives as one of the family will smell sweeter and feel fresher for the occasional bath. Using lukewarm water and a suitable dog shampoo (see the Sherley's range in Chapter 8), lather the dog all over, rinse well, and then repeat the process. The final rinse should be very thorough; to remove all traces of shampoo from the hair or the coat will be left with a dull, scurfy appearance. A shower attachment for the tap makes this job easier. Particular care should be taken when washing the head to avoid getting any lather in the eyes. A little Vaseline smeared over the lids will act as a protection.

Remove most of the moisture from the coat by rubbing with a dry towel, then complete the process with an electric hair dryer, providing that the dog is not frightened by it, or keep the dog in a warm place until it is completely dry. A final brush through the coat and you will have a dog to be proud of.

Insecticidal baths

Insecticidal baths may sometimes be necessary for the treatment of fleas, etc. These should be carried out strictly according to the manufacturer's instructions. Sherley's Insecticidal Shampoo is safe, effective, and straight-forward to use.

EARS

Ear care

The ears should be examined daily as part of the grooming routine. Long-eared breeds, such as spaniels and poodles, seem much more susceptible to ear trouble than the prick-eared breeds, probably because the flap of the ear prevents adequate ventilation of the ear canal. This is another example of the way in which man has caused quite unnecessary trouble to the dog, by breeding for appearance, instead of for soundness and health.

The ears may be cleaned if it is necessary to remove accumulations of wax. It is not wise for an inexperienced person to use any kind of probe to clean the ears, as the delicate inner surface of the ears may easily be damaged, especially if the dog jumps unexpectedly. Sherley's Ear Lotion is specially formulated to aid the removal of wax and other debris from the ear canal. It is gentle in action and does not irritate the ear.

Grass seeds

If your dog suddenly develops a painful ear (shown usually by holding the head on one side, crying, and shaking his head) especially following a walk in the grass, he may have a grass seed or barley awn in the ear. These are difficult to remove without expert advice, so it is best to consult a Veterinary Surgeon.

Persistent shaking of the head may also indicate that your dog has picked up ear mites, and these of course should be dealt with (see Chapter 5 – External Parasites).

An unpleasant or unusual smell from the ears, or any sign of discharge may indicate an infection and it is best to obtain some professional advice.

EYES

Eye care

Generally, no specific eye care is needed. Any eye problem will soon be obvious and it will probably require professional treatment. One related problem often seen by owners of light coloured dogs is a tearstain down the side of the nose. This can be difficult to remove, although it is only a cosmetic problem. However, Sherley's Eye Lotion is specially formulated to gently soothe and clean the eyes. It is suitable for use around the eyes, so aiding the removal of tearstains.

TEETH

The teeth should be cleaned daily, if the dog will allow, and special toothbrushes and toothpastes are now available from your pet shop. Sherley's make a meat-flavoured toothpaste, which is available with a specially designed toothbrush. Some dogs object a little at first, but they soon become accustomed to the treatment and the results are rewarding, in the form of cleaner teeth and sweeter breath. If the routine is started as a puppy, it will be easy to establish a regular routine. Never use human toothpastes though, as they contain foaming agents that are bad for your dog's stomach. Specially designed dental chews are also available which will help to keep the teeth and gums healthy.

TRIMMING AND STRIPPING

Many breeds of dogs, such as terriers, all of the rough-coated varieties (this includes West Highlands, Scotties, Airedales, and Wire-Haired Fox Terriers) and Spaniels require trimming, usually twice in the year, in spring and autumn, to get rid of their old coats and to keep them looking trim and tidy.

Poodles, on the other hand, have a very rapidly growing coat and need to be trimmed every six weeks if they are not to look like old sheep! This can obviously involve the owner in a lot of expense, and it is well worth learning to do the job yourself. You may never manage to achieve more than a neat appearance, but unless the dog is being shown this is quite sufficient, and for a nervous dog it can be less upsetting than being left in a poodle parlour.

Terriers

Terriers have a tough, hard coat that should be trimmed correctly by pulling or plucking the loose, hard hair. This is very laborious work unless you are an expert, so for a beginner it is a good idea to use either a trimming comb – a comb with an attached replaceable blade, and a pair of scissors, or to go to the initial expense of a good pair of electric clippers. A terrier when correctly trimmed should have a rather square, box-like appearance.
It is a good idea to get a picture of a show specimen from a magazine.

Spaniels

Spaniels should also be stripped using either a stripping knife, or a stripping comb. The coat should only be thinned and evened, not cut. Spaniels may be trimmed with electric clippers, but great care is needed to get a satisfactory, even appearance.

Poodles

Poodles are best trimmed with scissors only. Many people use clippers in the interest of speed, but Poodles have sensitive skins, and if the hair is cut too close, painful areas of clipping rash may occur, especially over the neck and sides of the face, which can be very slow to heal. For poodle trimming you will need a strong, sharp pair of pointed trimming scissors, a strong steel comb, with fairly close teeth, and a stiff brush. If you have groomed your dog regularly the job will be easy, but in any case there are no short cuts. If the finished results are to be satisfactory you must comb out all tangles, before you start to cut.

Style

By far the most popular, sensible, and from the dog's point of view, comfortable, poodle trim is the Lamb trim. In this the feet, muzzle, and base of tail are trimmed close, and the body coat is trimmed fairly short and even all over. Moustaches may be left if you wish. A Puppy trim is very similar, but the body coat is left longer as a protection against the weather. The more elaborate trims are the Lion, Dutch, and Continental. These are really only justifiable for those who want to show their dogs. The average owner wants a happy, clean, neat dog, not a fashion plate. See illustrations.

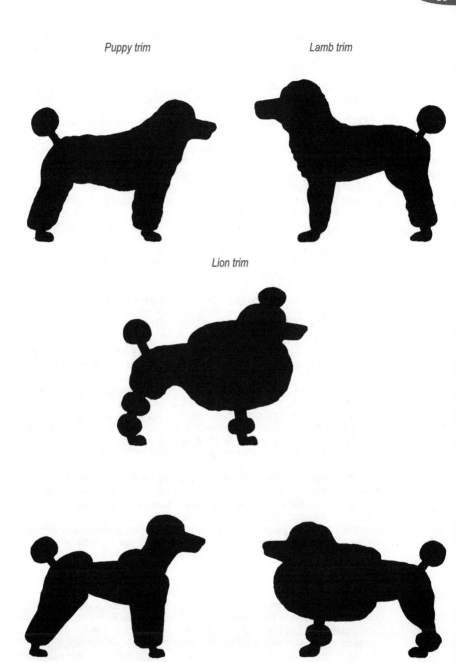

Puppy trim

Lamb trim

Lion trim

Dutch or Modern trim

Continental trim

Bedlington Terriers have woolly coats rather like poodles, and they are trimmed with scissors. The style is very much like a lamb, and again it is essential to get a picture of one correctly trimmed to use as a pattern.

Retrievers and Collies are not trimmed at all, but they can be much improved by a really thorough grooming, and having the hair thinned with a trimming comb.

HYGIENE AND DISINFECTION

Seven points

1. All dogs should be groomed daily, and checked for fleas, particularly during the summer.
2. All dogs should have their teeth cleaned regularly.
3. Bedding or blankets should be regularly washed.
4. Exercise areas should be kept clean, and disinfected where possible. Dogs, and especially puppies, shed roundworm eggs and there is risk of reinfection.
5. Following any case of skin disease such as ringworm or mange, it is of the greatest importance to destroy all bedding, including the box or basket. Do not forget the collar and lead as well.
6. Distemper is one of the most persistent infections. If there has been a case in a house remember that the virus can remain alive on furniture and carpets for a considerable time. It is wiser not to introduce an un-innoculated puppy into a house where there has been a case of distemper.
7. Let your dog have his own food dishes and see that they are kept separate and washed daily.

THE CORRECT DIET FOR YOUR DOG

Nutrition

The dog is a carnivore and in the wild state meat was his normal diet, but it should be realised that at this time he usually ate the whole of his kill to supply the protein, fats, minerals and vitamins that he needed. In order to supply him with all these nutrients, complete diets have been developed, which contain everything he needs, and can also be matched to his life-stage. It is difficult to generalise about the quantities of food that should be fed to a dog, as even within the different breeds there are great differences in the individual requirements. It is worth remembering though that if you are feeding more food than the dog needs to replace tissues, and to supply heat and energy for the body, it will be stored as fat, and a fat dog is not usually a fit, or happy one. It is perhaps a tribute to our kind hearts that obesity is now much more of a problem in dogs.

Quantity to feed

Time to feed

The dog is naturally adapted to eating at fairly infrequent intervals, and the food tends to remain in the stomach for a considerable time before digestion takes place. For the healthy dog, one or two meals a day is quite sufficient, given at regular times each day. Do not get into the habit of leaving a plate of biscuits down for your dog to nibble at through the day. It is not necessary if he is receiving a properly balanced diet, and the habit of eating through the day is as bad for a dog's figure as for ours. Never give your dog scraps at meal times, or worse still, feed him at the table. If he is to be given the scraps put them in his own dish, and give them at the proper time.

A dog which perpetually begs at the table is a nuisance (and his owner is to blame), and a dog which gets extras throughout the day will often be faddy and refuse his meals. A healthy dog, which is getting sufficient exercise and the right quantity of food, should be ready for its meals and clear them up at once. If your dog is choosy about the foods he will eat you are probably overfeeding him. Cut down drastically on the quantities you are offering over a few days, and his appetite will usually improve. On the other hand, if a normally hungry dog suddenly refuses his food this may be a sign of illness. If it continues for more than twenty four hours he probably needs professional attendance.

Sweets and treats

Do not start the bad habit of giving sweets or chocolate to your dog. They are not necessary and they may damage his teeth. Chocolate is positively harmful. A piece of cheese or a specially designed dog treat makes a better reward if it is necessary in training.

What to feed

If you do not wish to feed a "complete" diet, the meal should consist of part meat (or protein in some form) and part biscuit, the quantities of each varying according to the weight, age, and the amount of daily exercise.

A pregnant bitch or a growing pup may require considerably more food relative to its size than a normal adult dog. Equally, a dog living in a very cold climate will require extra food to maintain its body heat, and a Collie running all day on the hills will need more to supply energy.

A small dog may take meat only at the meal, with the addition of a hard biscuit or two to help the teeth. The meal for a large dog may consist of half biscuit and half meat. It is better to feed the biscuit fairly dry to give the dog something firm to chew on. Any gravy should be added at the last minute.

Protein

The protein part of your dog's diet may consist of fresh meat if it is available. It may be fed raw if it is absolutely fresh, but if there is any risk of contamination by flies it is better to boil it for a short time. If meat is to be stored in a refrigerator see that it is brought to room temperature before giving it to your dog, or you may find an attack of colic or stomach ache is the result.

Offal

Liver, heart, and kidneys have excellent food value, but in some dogs they may cause diarrhoea, so feed them cautiously at first. Tripe is a useful food, but lights, although they are very palatable to dogs, are low in food value.

Other foods

Fish, rabbit, or chicken are useful sources of protein and particularly valuable as invalid food, but great care should be taken to remove all bones. Eggs may be given if wished and beaten egg and milk makes a good tonic for a pregnant bitch or a dog in poor condition. Vegetables such as carrots or green vegetables may be included in a dog's diet if wished, but they are not essential.

Prepared foods

Nowadays, when convenience is important to us all, a great proportion of our dogs are fed partly, or wholly, on prepared dog foods. Those prepared by the leading manufacturers are very carefully formulated to supply all the nutrients required for a dog's health and although they are, on the face of it, fairly expensive to buy, there is no waste, and the actual value compares well with meat bought from the butcher. Prepared foods may come in the form of tinned foods, which usually have a high moisture content, semi-moist foods prepared in packets, or sachets, or as a complete dried diet.

Care should be taken to check with the manufacturer's description as to whether the food is an all-meat product intended for mixing with biscuits, or if it contains a proportion of cereal as well.

Bones

Dogs certainly enjoy bones and they do have some value in keeping the teeth clean, but they should be given only with caution. Really large marrow bones when they are available are excellent, but any bones which the dog can break up and splinter are dangerous. Sharp bones such as chicken or rabbit should never be given, and small bones such as chops are equally dangerous. They can only too easily be swallowed whole and they may become lodged at the entrance to the stomach, or in the intestine, with sometimes fatal results. Soft bones are less dangerous, but when chewed up and swallowed they form a hard concrete-like mass in the bowel and may cause a bad case of constipation. It is worth mentioning that a dog which has eaten a bone will normally pass a very characteristic hard whitish motion.

You may possibly be thinking that dogs in the wild state must have eaten bones and this is obviously true, but a certain number of them died as a result, and you would not wish this to happen to your pet.

Dog chews or mock bones made from hide are useful for the dog who really loves something to chew, or for puppies which are cutting teeth, and they are free from the disadvantages of real bones.

TRAVEL

Motoring manners

Most dogs love to travel by car once they become accustomed to it. Indeed, many dogs seem to be happy just to sit in a stationary car, pretending it is going along. However, if a journey is to be a pleasure for both dog and owner too, it is important that your dog should learn good car manners. Let him have his own place on the seat, or on the floor, with his own rug. Do not allow him to leap from the front to the back of the car when something attracts his attention outside, or to hang his head out of the window. The first is very dangerous for the driver, and the second is liable to cause sore eyes. A good dog barrier for the rear of an estate car is a sound investment.

A dog bag is a very useful thing to keep in the car. This is shaped like a pillow case, in a size appropriate to the dog, and made of strong towelling or any strong material. You can pop your dog into it after a muddy walk, fastening it around the neck if necessary. By the time you get home you will have a drier, cleaner dog, and a clean car!

Car sickness

Many dogs or puppies are sick at their first experience of car travel, but in most cases they soon get over it, especially if they are only taken on short journeys at first, with a nice run at the end. For the dog that is persistently sick, extra care must be taken. Give a short walk before the journey, and do not give a meal for at least two hours before. If the problem still persists it is advisable to get in touch with your local Veterinary Surgeon.

Try to avoid leaving your dog in the car, if at all possible. If it is unavoidable, great care should be taken to provide adequate ventilation. Leave all windows open a little way to provide a draught, or better still get a wire mesh window guard. Leave the car in a shady place, remembering that the position of the sun will alter. Each year dogs die from heat stroke or suffocation as a result of owners lack of care.

Train travel

If you are travelling by train you may be allowed to keep your dog with you in the compartment, but you may be asked to produce a muzzle, or to place him in the guard's van, at the discretion of the train staff.

Air travel

When travelling by plane, whether with you, or unaccompanied, your dog or puppy will have to travel in a crate in the luggage compartment. This is liable to be both noisy and cold, so it is as well to provide a warm blanket, and in the case of a nervous dog, consult a Veterinary Surgeon. If you are travelling abroad with your dog the firm which is arranging your transport will usually take care of the arrangements for your dog as well. If you are sending a dog on its own you will be wise to put yourself in the hands of a firm specialising in this work.

QUARANTINE REGULATIONS

UK quarantine regulations were phased out in April 2001. They are replaced by the new "Movement for Pets Scheme" which enables dogs and cats coming from European Union countries, other European countries, and rabies-free islands to enter the UK without quarantine. The system also covers UK resident cats and dogs that have been abroad temporarily in those countries. Pets from other countries will continue to be subject to quarantine regulations , although the USA and Canada's position is being reviewed.

For further information on UK quarantine and the new regulations contact the Department for Environment, Food and Rural Affairs (or if in Scotland the Department of Agriculture and Fisheries for Scotland).

TAKING YOUR DOG ABROAD

When taking your dog out of the United Kingdom you will require a certificate of health given by a Veterinary Surgeon within a few days of leaving.

In addition, some countries require your dog to be vaccinated against rabies, or to produce a certificate showing that it is free from leptospirosis or other diseases. In some countries there is also a short quarantine period on arrival, but because the United Kingdom is free from rabies most places will admit British dogs at once. It really is important to find out all these details about the country concerned as soon as possible. Your Veterinary Surgeon will often be able to help you find out what is required. Failure to do this may involve you in considerable delay, or heartbreak, if you find that you are unable to take your pet with you.

PUTTING YOUR DOG IN KENNELS

If your circumstances make it probable that you will have to put your dog in kennels from time to time, it is as well to get him used to it as early in his life as possible. Young dogs, if they have been sensibly brought up to be reasonably independent, will usually take to kennel life quite well. An older dog, which has only known its own home is more likely to be distressed and to feel that you have left it forever.

Do go and see the kennels for yourself in good time before your holidays. If they are clean and well run you can have an easy mind, and if they are not you have time to make other arrangements. It is no use deciding when your plane is just about to leave that the place is quite unsuitable. Let your dog take his own bed and blanket with him so that he feels less isolated and far from home. Check that the food at the kennels is something that he is used to, or offer to take a supply of his regular food. Most conscientious kennel proprietors now require a certificate of vaccination against the major preventable diseases so check in good time to see if your dog requires a booster injection; this is usually given annually. It is also a good idea to equip your dog with a Sherley's Flea Collar beforehand – it could save you the trouble of getting rid of the odd flea on his return.

When you return, try not to blame the kennels if your dog has lost weight, or has lost his voice. Very few kennel owners would be likely to keep a dog short of food, but many dogs will fret and refuse to eat, and others will bark until they are hoarse, when they find themselves suddenly left in a strange place.

If your dog is really unhappy in kennels, try to make an arrangement with a dog-owning friend to look after each other's dogs at holiday time or better still take your dog with you if possible.

BAD HABITS AND HOW TO DEAL WITH THEM

Neuroses

Some of the bad habits of the dog may be generally classified as a return to primitive behaviour. After all, the wild dog needed to chase and kill game, but this is not acceptable in a civilised world. Other behaviour problems seem to relate more to human neuroses. For instance, dogs who suddenly become frightened of traffic, or terrified of being left alone in a room. Presumably something happened to disturb them, which they connect with a particular place, but it is very difficult for us to understand, or deal with the situation. It is worth remembering that the dog is, by nature, a pack animal and in the absence of a pack leader, he appreciates firm guidance from his owner as a substitute.

If you have brought your dog up from a pup, by the time he is fully grown he should be a reasonably well trained companion. However, if you take over the care of an adult dog, you may have some difficult behaviour problems to deal with. Some of these can be overcome by kind and sensible treatment, but others if they are of long standing may prove impossible to eradicate.

Temper-ament

As the various breeds of dog become more inbred, in the pursuit of show appearance, they seem to become worse in temperament. It is getting increasingly difficult to point to any one breed and say that it is 100% reliable. Even Cocker Spaniels, which were once a most placid breed are now often nervous and snappy, and the golden or red strains seem to be the most highly strung of all.

Remember that if you get a large dog this problem is going to be intensified. It is possible to live with a savage Pekinese, but a savage German Shepherd or Rottweiller is a different proposition. It is probably true to say overall, though, that bitches are less aggressive and make better pets than dogs. While dogs may inherit a tendency to be placid or nervous, a great deal depends on their upbringing. If you are always kind, firm, and above all consistent with your dog, you will get a good response. On the other hand, if you are excitable and inclined to "fly off the handle" do not be surprised if your dog behaves in the same way.

Biting

Never tease your puppy, or allow children to do so, and never encourage your puppy to growl or bite, even in fun. It may seem amusing in a little pup, but is much less so in an adult dog.

It is sad to say that a dog which has once bitten its owner will almost certainly do so again. In these circumstances you should pause and think very seriously as to whether this is a risk that you are prepared to take, particularly if there are children in the house. A dog which is really vicious should be painlessly destroyed. It is neither kind nor fair to give it to someone else.

Postmen

Biting a postman has, regrettably, always been considered something of a joke, but obviously it is no joke to the postman. Unfortunately, many dogs who are trained to bark and guard the house take a great dislike to some of the routine callers and especially those in uniform. It is worth taking time to introduce your dog to these people, if they are dog lovers, so that your dog accepts that they are welcome visitors, If this proves impossible, make sure that the dog is not left to roam unsupervised in the garden.

Fighting

It may sound something of a contradiction, but it is often the more nervous and timid dogs which become fighters. It seems that they feel that attack is the best form of defence. An over-protective attitude on the part of the owner usually makes this situation worse. If you rush to pick up your dog as soon as another dog approaches, it gives the impression that there is something to fear. Try to exercise your dog right from the start in company with a friend's dog, so that he becomes less apprehensive of his own kind.

If your dog shows a tendency to attack other dogs while on the lead he must be checked. Stand still while the other dog walks past. Speak very sternly to your dog if he growls and make him sit. As his behaviour improves, still make him stop and sit while other dogs go past and then pat him and praise him.

CHASING

Sheep chasing

This must count as the worst vice that a dog can have and it is a serious worry for those who live in the country. A dog which is seen chasing sheep, or even seen in suspicious circumstances, may be shot by the farmer, and for this reason country dogs, just as much as those that live in the town, should never be allowed to wander on their own. The law that allows farmers this right may sound harsh, but terrible damage is inflicted on sheep and lambs each year by wandering or straying dogs. When training your dog, take every opportunity to walk it on the lead through fields where there are sheep and cattle. If the dog shows the slightest interest say "No" in a very stern voice.

Cars and bicycles

This, though it is less common than some other bad habits, can be an equally difficult problem. Some dogs seem to be really maddened by the sound of an engine and something stronger than them comes over them and they are of course quite deaf to all your calls. If caught early, the habit may be checked by exercising your dog on the lead in traffic, and making it sit and wait calmly as each car goes by. However, if the habit has become really ingrained the only measure you can take is to see that the dog is never allowed to get out on its own. He could be the cause of a serious accident.

Cats

Chasing cats should never be encouraged, even as a game. A dog can easily kill a kitten which has not learned to realise the danger, or a dog may be badly scratched by an older cat. Dogs and cats can live very happily in the same household when they get used to each other, and there is quite enough strife in the world without our encouraging it.

DESTRUCTIVENESS

Chewing

This problem has already been discussed as it affects younger dogs. Most pups will chew up the occasional shoe if they get the chance, but if an older dog continues to destroy furniture or doors or wallpaper we must look further for the reason.

This sort of behaviour is most common in dogs which have had to change homes or have lacked a secure and reassuring start in life.

Make sure that the dog is getting as much exercise as possible – a tired dog is much less likely to be a destructive one. Concentrate on making the dog stay in his own bed, while you are in the room, so that he understands that this is where he is expected to stay.

Toys

Give him some strong toys of his own to chew if he wants, and of course confine him to one room where you have put everything possible out of reach. Sometimes leaving the radio on when you go out will provide a little reassurance. This can be a very difficult and expensive time in a dog owner's life, but don't despair – it won't last for ever.

False pregnancy

Bitches will sometimes show symptoms of false pregnancy about eight or nine weeks after a season. In this state they really imagine that they have puppies, and start to scratch up their blankets to make a bed for the imaginary offspring. So if you come home one day to find your normally well-behaved bitch has chewed up her blankets, this may be the reason.

COPROPHAGIA

Practical measures

Young dogs will sometimes develop the very unpleasant habit of eating their own faeces – usually to the great dismay of their owners. It has been suggested that this indicates a dietary deficiency, but there is no conclusive evidence. If you are satisfied that your dog is in good physical condition there is no need to worry too much. The problem can usually be dealt with by taking simple practical measures. Never leave your dog alone in the garden or yard, and see that all faeces are cleared away, and disinfectant put down at once. Sprinkling pepper, or other unpleasant substances does not seem to deter dogs from this particular habit at all. There are in-feed products now available to combat this type of behaviour. Your local pet shop or Veterinary Surgeon should be able to give you further information. When exercising, keep your dog on a lead, or at least until he has passed a motion, and you have got him well away from the place. Once again, this really is something that they will grow out of.

DOG SHOWS AND KENNEL CLUB REGULATIONS

Dog shows in England have been held since 1859, starting with a very simple show for pointers and setters. Today, showing dogs has become immensely popular, and shows are held all over the country for the many different breeds, culminating each year with Crufts Dog Show in Birmingham. Here the top dogs of all varieties are seen, and dog breeders and dog lovers from all over the world attend. The Kennel Club, which holds the register of all pedigree dogs was formed in 1873, and since that time has done a great deal to promote concern for dogs, and their welfare.

Unfortunately, it was not realised that the rather intensive inbreeding of dogs to produce their attractive show points was also leading to the appearance of some very unwelcome inherited faults. Among these we can include the condition known as hip dysplasia in German Shepherd Dogs, and the enlarged soft palate of some of the short-nosed breeds such as pugs, which makes it difficult for them to breath. Nowadays responsible breeders are trying to see that health and soundness of the dog is the first consideration, and it may be said that overall the showing of dogs has done much more good than harm.

Only registered pedigree dogs may be exhibited at shows organised under Kennel Club rules, but if you own a cross-breed pup you may often find a show in your district, where prizes are given for appearance, obedience, or charm.

REGISTERING YOUR PUP

A pedigree dog is one whose dam and sire were both entered in the Kennel Club register. If your new puppy is a thoroughbred the breeder will supply you with a written pedigree and register your puppy. This is done by writing to the Kennel Club at their headquarters at 1 Clarges Street, Piccadilly, London, W1Y 8AB (telephone number 08706 066750).

PREPARING YOUR DOG FOR SHOW

Faults

If your dog is to be shown, he must of course be in tiptop condition. In the breeds where trimming is required, there is a case for getting expert advice from a breeder. It is a good idea to buy a book about your particular breed to learn all you can about the subject, and to get a good picture in your own mind of the show points, and the appearance of a good specimen of the breed.
When you are choosing a pup with a view to showing, check to see that it is free from any obvious faults such as over or under shot jaw, or kinks in the tail. If you are very inexperienced take an expert friend with you, or ask to buy the pup subject to a satisfactory examination by a Veterinary Surgeon. It can be very disappointing to pay a high price for a pup, only to find that it is of no use for showing.

Health inspection

All dogs should be vaccinated, and this is of special importance if you are attending shows, as at any place where a lot of dogs are gathered together the risk of infection is high. At all shows run under the Kennel Club Rules a Veterinary Surgeon examines each dog before it is admitted, and if he suspects that there is any infection which might be passed on to other animals, the dog will be refused entry.

While showing your dog can be a pleasant hobby, if you mean to take it seriously and if you have the good fortune to have picked a good dog, it can take up a lot of time, and involve a certain amount of expense. Breed shows are held all over the country and if your dog is to become a champion it is necessary to attend the appropriate shows to meet the competition.

INTERNAL AND ,EXTERNAL PARASITES OF THE DOG

INTERNAL PARASITES

Worms

Of all the subjects which cause anxiety to owners concerning their dog's health, worms can be placed at the top of the list. Over the years a great deal of superstition and mythology has built up regarding the supposed symptoms caused by worms and the weird and horrific folk remedies which were used to get rid of them. There is really no need for this excessive alarm. Firstly, worms do not cause a great number of conditions which are attributed to them and secondly, with modern drugs they can be quite safely eliminated without causing any distress to the patient.

All dogs, at some time in their lives, have worms. Usually this is during their puppyhood, and at this time the owner should treat routinely for worms, whether symptoms are obvious or not. A dog that appears quite healthy can be carrying worms, may pass or vomit a worm, and be shedding hundreds or thousands of worm eggs in their faeces.

There has been a great deal of publicity in recent years regarding the risk of infection to children through contamination of parks and playgrounds by faeces from dogs infected with roundworms (see "Danger to Children" later in chapter). What is not generally realised is the fact that control of these worms by the regular dosing of dogs with products such as Sherley's range of roundworm medicines is cheap, effective and harmless to the pets. If all dogs were regularly treated, the risk to human health could be minimised.

Roundworms and tapeworms

The worms found in dogs in Britain fall into two main categories; roundworms and tapeworms. They are not blood-sucking worms, but live on the partly digested food material in the stomach and intestine. Unless they are present in very large quantities they are unlikely to produce symptoms of illness, except in the case of young puppies. If you see definite signs of worms (see "What to look for") you should, both for the dog's sake and in the interest of hygiene, take measures to get rid of them. However, if your dog becomes ill, never assume that worms are the cause and commence treatment without consulting a Veterinary Surgeon.

ROUNDWORMS (TOXOCARA CANIS)

Recognition

Roundworms, also called ascarids, are mainly of importance in young puppies and pregnant bitches. They only infrequently cause problems in dogs of two years and over. However, these animals still carry infections, and continue to shed worm eggs to reinfect other dogs.

In appearance they are round-bodied, rather similar to a tiny earth worm. They can be up to nine inches in length but are usually much smaller, and are of whitish colour or pinkish brown due to ingested material.

How they spread

The life cycle of the roundworm is quite simple. They are spread directly from dog to dog. The eggs, which are microscopic in size and invisible to the naked eye, are passed in the faeces. They are ingested again by licking, and when swallowed develop in the intestines of the dog into larvae, or microscopic immature worms. These migrate through the blood stream to the lungs. They are then coughed up and swallowed again. These larvae grow to maturity in the intestines and begin producing eggs, so completing the life cycle. The adult worms are sometimes noticed at this time when they may be vomited or passed in the faeces.

Need to dose more than once

In young puppies, there is no natural immunity to worms, and this cycle readily completes without interference. Since puppies constantly reinfect themselves and each other, there is a need to repeat treatment on a two-weekly basis (see "Treatment"), as wormers have no residual effect.

As the dog matures, it develops an immunity to the worms, and is able to put up a degree of self-defence. In the adult dog, this immune reaction causes the majority of developing larvae to become trapped in the dog's muscles as harmless cysts. As fewer worms make it all the way to the intestine, treatment is needed less frequently, and intervals of three months are recommended between treatments. However, if female dogs later become pregnant, the resulting drop in immunity brought about by hormonal changes allow trapped larvae to break out of their cysts and resume their travels around her body. At this time, some of the larvae will cross the placenta and enter the unborn puppies. Virtually all puppies are born with worms, and treatment of the bitch and litter is essential from two weeks of age onwards (see "Treatment").

Roundworms

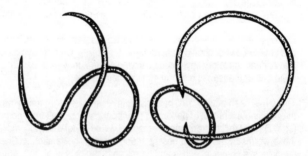

What to look for

Symptoms of worm burdens can vary from quite serious to very mild. In young pups worms may cause abdominal distensions and pain, loss of weight, vomiting or diarrhoea and even, on rare occasions, rupture of the bowel. At post-mortem examination the stomach and intestines of these pups may be found to contain hundreds of worms. The migrating larvae in the lungs may also cause coughing, which can be an important symptom. These larvae may also travel through the liver, brain or other tissues.

Treatment

Modern treatment for roundworms does not necessitate starving the dog, and usually causes no distress at all. The remedies are palatable and easy to administer, and generally are very effective. Puppies should be treated from two weeks of age, and the treatment repeated at fortnightly intervals up to three months of age. At each of these treatments the bitch should also be treated. Remember that reinfection can easily occur. Thereafter, treat the pups every four weeks until twenty-four weeks of age. After this, they can be treated according to the recommended adult regime of once every three to four months.

Treatment of the in-whelp bitch

It is possible to administer worming treatments to pregnant bitches, but great care should be taken in selecting a suitable product. Read the label carefully before purchasing, and check that the product is safe to use during pregnancy. If in any doubt, contact the manufacturer or your Veterinary Surgeon. Sherley's One Dose Wormer can be used safely throughout all stages of pregnancy.

What wormer to use

Unfortunately, wormers do not exist, either from your pet shop or your Veterinary Surgeon, that are able to kill the larvae trapped in the cysts in the body, so timing of treatment of the pregnant bitch is very important if ante-natal infection of the puppies is to be prevented. Only one type of wormer, available only from your Veterinary Surgeon, is recommended for this use, and needs to be given to the bitch every day for a period of 25 days. Even this is not 100% effective. You may prefer to wait until your bitch has had her puppies, and then treat both her and the litter together.

Adult dogs only need treatment every three months unless they become pregnant.

There are many products available to treat roundworms. The Sherley's range is listed in Chapter 8.

Unweaned puppies need only be treated for roundworm, but following weaning, tapeworms should also be considered. Read the label of each product before buying, to ensure it is recommended for use in your own pet. If in doubt, ask the pet shop owner or your Veterinary Surgeon for further advice.

Danger to children

Although the roundworm cannot complete its life cycle in humans, ingested eggs can cause serious, though fortunately rare, conditions in children. They hatch into larvae in the gut and can then migrate to various organs of the body, including the liver, lungs, eyes, and brain, where they can become permanently encysted. It is therefore of the greatest importance to see that puppies which are in contact with children are kept free from worms, and that a good standard of hygiene is maintained. The dog's excreta should be cleared away as soon as possible from gardens or exercise runs to prevent the ground becoming heavily contaminated with worm eggs, which can lay dormant in the topsoil for several years. Likewise, dogs should be discouraged from fouling public places where children play.

N.B. worm eggs found in fresh faeces are not infective, so there is no danger to you if you clear up after your dog straightaway.

TAPEWORMS (TAENIA AND DIPYLIDIUM SPECIES)

Tapeworms are most commonly found in the adult dog. It always has to be remembered that tapeworms have to have an intermediate host (i.e. spend a part of their life in another animal), and therefore successful treatment includes elimination of the intermediate host as well as removing the adult worms from the dog.

Recognition

This worm consists of a number of whitish coloured segments which are joined together to form the tape, terminating at the narrow end in a head which is attached by minute hooks to the lining of the intestines of the dog.

They vary in length from a few cm, to 5 m, but it is more often the individual segments (containing the eggs) which are seen as they are shed in the faeces. These may appear as short strings of white segments, or white wriggling particles, looking like grains of rice, in the faeces (they are often mistakenly described by owners as roundworms), or attached to the hair in the tail region.

How they spread

Tapeworms are never transmitted directly from dog to dog, but always through an intermediate host. These may include birds, mice, rabbits and lice, but the most common one for town dogs is the flea. The dog may swallow the flea containing the larvae of the tapeworm while grooming, or may be infected while hunting rabbits, etc. or eating uncooked animal carcasses. The larva grows into a tapeworm and attaches itself to the intestine of the dog where it remains until it is mature and commences to shed segments containing the microscopic eggs. These eggs are then eaten by the intermediate host to repeat the cycle.

What to look for?

Except in the case of massive infestation, digestive symptoms do not occur. Tapeworms do not usually cause loss of weight, and fat dogs as well as thin ones may be heavily infested. The dog may show signs of anal irritation as a result of shedding segments but it should be noted that this is rarely the case. Most dogs showing irritation around their hind end are, in fact, not infected by worms but have problems with their anal glands.

Control of the intermediate host

Treatment should be carried out both for the sake of the dog, and for aesthetic and hygienic reasons. If reinfestation is to be avoided, measures must be taken to get rid of the intermediate host. In the case of fleas this involves regular bathing or spraying with a suitable insecticide, such as Sherley's Insecticidal Shampoo, Sherley's Flea Spray, Sherley's Big Red Flea Spray, (see later section on fleas) or the wearing of a Sherley's Insecticidal Collar. For those dogs that are inveterate hunters and rely on other intermediate hosts to keep up their tapeworm infestation, the only answer is a regular dosing with tapeworm remedies. Cooking meat will destroy tapeworm cysts.

Tapeworm showing the head on the left

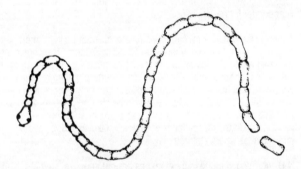

Treatment

Tapeworms may sometimes prove rather difficult to eliminate as unless the head, or scolex, is destroyed the worm will soon start to grow again, even though a considerable part of the tape has been shed. If segments start to appear immediately after dosing it suggests that the treatment has not been fully effective and should be repeated, taking care to use a preparation that is designed specifically for tapeworm. If segments appear after a few weeks it is more likely that reinfestation has taken place and you should ensure that you are also dealing with the intermediate host of the tapeworm at the same time as you repeat the treatment.

What wormer to use

Sherley's tapeworm treatments are listed in Chapter 8. Make sure that you select a product suitable for your own pet.

Danger to humans

Dog tapeworms are only very rarely transmitted to humans. However, infestation with echinococcus, a less common species, can very occasionally occur, and may be serious.

HOOKWORMS (UNCINARIA)

Other worm parasites

These are much less commonly seen in Britain, but they are blood-sucking worms and can cause serious loss of condition. They are susceptible to treatment with some drugs (for example, it will be killed by Sherley's One Dose Wormer, if it is present), but if in any doubt consult a Veterinary Surgeon.

WHIPWORMS (TRICHURIS)

This is a rather rare type of worm infestation which would be diagnosed by a Veterinary Surgeon since they are unlikely to be observed by owners.

EXTERNAL PARASITES

Fleas, lice and ticks

Even under present day conditions, dogs are liable to become infected with the common ectoparasites, that is to say the parasites which live in, or on the skin. You may feel that because your house is kept spotlessly clean this is unlikely to happen, but any dog which is taken out for exercise and socialises with other dogs can pick up fleas, lice or less commonly ticks, and suffer accordingly. Indeed, these parasites actually prefer to live in a clean coat.

Make a point of giving your dog a thorough grooming several times a week and keep a careful watch for these parasites, especially in the summer months when they are most prevalent.

The best form of prevention is to be prepared before a problem takes hold. Ideally, treat your house (carpets in all rooms to which your dog has access, soft furnishing and bedding) with one of Sherley's household flea products before the beginning of the "flea season" (i.e. April is ideal). These products give effective long-lasting control for up to one year.

Additionally, you may wish to give your pet a dusting with Flea Powder or use Sherley's Insecticidal Shampoo occasionally as a precautionary measure. Sherley's flea collars are also available and used correctly provide prolonged protection. See the Sherley's range of anti-parasitic products in Chapter 8.

Without suitable treatment flea eggs and larvae can persist in carpets and upholstery for many weeks.

Symptoms

The first sign of parasitic infestation that you will notice is persistent scratching and loss of hair. If you fail to take action on this you may then be confronted with open sores, where the dog has bitten or scratched itself raw as a result of intense irritation.

It seems that some dogs, like some people, are much more attractive to these insects and you may find that where two dogs are kept together one will be constantly attacked by fleas or lice while the other remains apparantly flea-free.

Transmission

Fortunately, there is little risk of transmission to humans. Dog lice never attack people, dog fleas will occasionally, and ticks only very infrequently, usually in moorland districts. None of these parasites will breed on people.

THE FLEA

By far the most common flea found on dogs is the cat flea (Ctenocephalides felis). Much more rare is the dog flea (Ctenocephalides canis). Very occasionally hedgehog fleas are also found. Even rarer still are human fleas, rabbit fleas, and bird fleas. Fleas are most common in summer and autumn when it is warm enough for their life cycle to be completed in a short time. However, with the advent of central heating household infestations can occur even in winter months.

The adult flea spends all its life on the dog, where it feeds, breeds, and lays eggs. The eggs are extremely smooth and non-sticky so that they fall out of the pet's coat easily and drop onto carpets or bedding. After a few days they hatch into tiny larvae which feed on dust, debris, and adult flea faeces until they form a pupa. The pupa disguises itself with particles of dust and fluff which are stuck to its outer casing. In the pupal stage, the flea life cycle can remain dormant for up to twelve months just waiting for an increase in temperature or the vibration made by a pet walking close by. Once the pupa hatches, a young juvenile flea is released and begins its search for a host to live on to continue the life cycle. At the height of summer this life cycle from egg to flea may take as little as three weeks.

Recognition

Fleas are blackish brown, shiny and roughly one-sixteenth of an inch in size. They tend to run very rapidly, through the coat rather than to jump, and can be quite difficult to detect. They may sometimes be found in clusters on the abdomen, or at the base of the tail. They are blood-sucking insects, and their characteristic black, ash-like excreta can very readily be seen on the dog's coat or on the bedding.

Symptoms

The dog will start to scratch and there may be loss of hair. Later bare places will develop and there may be open sores especially at the base of the tail.

Treatment

Treatment by the use of any Sherley's flea product (see Chapter 8) is usually very effective. Blankets should be washed if possible and all boxes or baskets disinfected or sprayed with an insecticide such as Sherley's Defest II, as should any other place where the dog spends time lying.

Treatment

To prevent reinfection Sherley's Flea Collars are an easy solution. These are thin collars impregnated with insecticide which is slowly released over time, and gives continuous protection for up to four months. See the Sherley's range in Chapter 8.

Flea life cycle

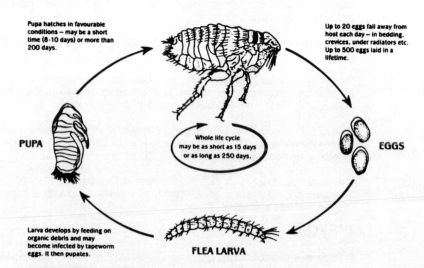

ADULT FLEA

Pupa hatches in favourable conditions – may be a short time (8-10 days) or more than 200 days.

Up to 20 eggs fall away from host each day – in bedding, crevices, under radiators etc. Up to 500 eggs laid in a lifetime.

PUPA

Whole life cycle may be as short as 15 days or as long as 250 days.

EGGS

Larva develops by feeding on organic debris and may become infected by tapeworm eggs. It then pupates.

FLEA LARVA

Hedgehog fleas – If at any time your dog finds a hedgehog in the garden he may come in with his ears or face covered with tiny black insects. These are hedgehog fleas, and while they may cause mild discomfort for a very short time, they do not live on dogs. Treatment, using a flea powder or spray, is very quickly effective, but be very careful to avoid eyes, nostrils, mouth, and inner ears.

THE COMMON DOG LOUSE

Recognition Lice are only rarely found on dogs. The dog louse (also called Trichodectes canis) is tiny, pinkish-white in colour, and rather spherical in shape. They are quite slow-moving and attach themselves to the dog's skin, where they feed. They may be found all over the body, but more especially in the hair of the ears, particularly of the long-eared breeds. The eggs, or nits as they are called, have very much the appearance of scurf. However, if they are examined under a magnifying glass it will be seen that they are oval and shiny, and that each one is firmly attached to an individual hair. Lice can also be intermediate hosts for the tapeworm.

Symptoms Persistent scratching, loss of hair and sore places, especially on the flaps of the ears.

In very young pups severe pediculosis or infestation with lice can, on very rare occasions, lead to anaemia and even death.

Treatment Consult your Veterinary Surgeon for a product suitable against lice.

Dog louse

Common tick

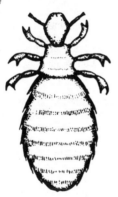
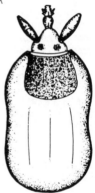

TICKS

Recognition Ticks (ixodes and other species) are bluish black and bean-like in appearance. Their size varies, but they may be up to half an inch in diameter when engorged with blood. At this stage they are sometimes mistaken for a skin cyst. Examination under a magnifying glass will show the presence of legs and a biting mouthpiece, by which the tick is attached to the dog.
Ticks are found mainly on moors and in country districts where they are normally parasitic on sheep but they will attach themselves to a dog, or very rarely to a person, if the opportunity occurs.

Ticks are also found on hedgehogs, and this is sometimes the source of infestation in town dogs.

Treatment Ticks should first be sprayed with a suitable insecticide and then, where individual ticks are found, they may usually be removed with tweezers, after applying a piece of cotton wool soaked in surgical spirit or an antiseptic lotion, taking care not to leave in place the biting head, or an abscess may form. Ticks will drop off on their own accord after a few days, when they have finished feeding. Alternatively, you can use Sherley's Tick Away, an easy-to-use spray for simple removal of ticks from your dogs.

HARVEST MITES

These are harvest bugs which cause considerable annoyance to humans as well as dogs in the country during the late summer. They are actually a kind of mite, and in dogs they are found most frequently in the skin between the toes or up the length of the leg. They are just visible to the naked eye, and groups of them have a red or yellowish appearance.

Consult your Veterinary Surgeon for a product suitable against harvest mites.

CHEYLETIELLA PARASITOVORAX

This is another form of microscopic mite, and is often difficult to recognise. There is irritation and usually a very thick white scurf forms, mainly along the back of the infected animal. If the scurf is examined accurately it may be seen to move.

Treatment is very similar to that of Sarcoptic Mange (see later) and it is usually best to consult your Veterinary Surgeon if you believe your dog has this condition. Repeat treatment is frequently required. This mite may also cause a rash on humans, particularly young children.

THE EAR MITE

This mite (Otodectes cynotis) is of considerable importance to the dog owner, as it lives only in the ear canal of dogs (and cats) where it causes great irritation. The dog reacts to this by shaking the head and scratching, causing exudation, and sometimes haemorrhage and thus pre-disposing to many of the intractable and chronic ear conditions which are seen. Cats, while they are very susceptible to ear mites, appear to be less sensitive to them. The condition in cats, and especially young kittens, is sometimes not suspected until a dog living in the house picks up the infection, and immediately shows his discomfort.

Recognition
Ear mites are just visible to the naked eye as pin point greyish dots, and they are easily visible under a magnifying glass. The main symptom is persistent shaking or scratching of the ears. On examination the ears are often found to be full of dry, dark brown wax.

Treatment
If the diagnosis is certain, relief can quickly be obtained by the application of ear drops designed to destroy mites. This should be repeated at weekly intervals to catch the new mites as they emerge from the eggs. If the condition has persisted for some time, secondary bacterial infection is almost certain to have taken place and veterinary advice should be sought.

Grass seeds
A sudden onset of violent head shaking, especially after a walk through long grass, may indicate the presence of a grass seed in the ear, rather than an ear mite infection, and in this case also veterinary help will be needed.

There are three other important external parasites which can affect the dog. These are not visible to the naked eye, and they can only be definitely diagnosed by microscopic examination of a scraping of skin from the affected animal. They comprise of two types of mange, and ringworm, and they are of special interest because in the case of two of them there is considerable risk of transmission to man, particularly where dogs are allowed to sleep on chairs or beds.

SARCOPTIC MANGE

This is the most common type of mange, and it is caused by the mite Scarcoptes scabiei. This mite burrows into the superficial layers of the dog's skin where it lives and lays its eggs causing intense irritation to its host. It is most common in puppies and young dogs, and it may become a serious problem in kennels if proper hygienic measures are not taken to control it.

Recognition
In the early stages, sarcoptic mange is characterised by persistent scratching, followed as a result

of this, by the appearance of reddish patches of inflammation of the axilla (arm pits) and on the inside of the thighs. There are often bare places around the eyes and scaly thickening of the ear flaps. The condition, if not checked, may spread all over the body of the dog with the formation of scabs, sores, and bare places throughout the coat. There may be a general loss of condition as a result of the constant irritation. Diagnosis may be confirmed by a Veterinary Surgeon who will examine a skin scraping taken from one of the affected places under a microscope.

Trans-mission

Sarcoptic mange is readily transmissible both to other dogs and to people when it is known as scabies. Children are especially susceptible, probably because of their more delicate skin, and the fact that they are more likely to come in close contact with their pets while playing.

In humans the first signs of infection are usually red irritable patches on the fingers or wrists. If you have any reason to suspect infection consult your doctor as soon as possible.

Treatment

Advice on a suitable course of treatment should be sought from your Veterinary Surgeon.

The dog should not be allowed to come into contact with other animals. The bedding should be boiled each week and the basket or box, as well as all collars and harnesses, thoroughly scrubbed with disinfectant.

Any swabs or cotton wool used for applying skin dressing should be disposed of by burning if possible. The owner should remember the importance of washing the hands each time after handling or dressing the dog.

Finally, remember that because mange mites live in the layers of the skin it is hard to be certain when they have been totally eliminated. It is necessary therefore to persevere with treatment and hygienic measures for some time after the external symptoms have disappeared, or you may be disappointed by a recurrence of the problem.

DEMODECTIC OR FOLLICULAR MANGE

This type of mange is caused by Demodex canis, a rather cigar-shaped mite recognisable only under a microscope. This mite lives in the deeper layers of the skin, coming to the skin surface only intermittently in its life cycle. It will be understood therefore that it is a much more difficult condition to treat effectively.

Recognition

Initially, the appearance of dry scaly places in the dog's coat may be seen. Short-coated varieties, and in particular Dachshunds and Dobermans, seem to be most often affected and the dog may have a rather characteristic "musty" or "mousy" odour. The bare places may remain quiescent for some time but usually, as a result of scratching, bacterial infection follows, often with the presence of very resistant staphylococci and formation of small discharging pustules or abscesses. The dog's skin tends to become thickened and wrinkled, especially on the limbs, and if the condition is not checked it may lead to a severe illness or even death as a result of a generalised bacterial infection or septicaemia.

Diagnosis

Diagnosis may be confirmed, as with sarcoptic mange, by a skin scraping, but it is sometimes less easy to demonstrate the presence of mites, because of their tendency to invade the deeper tissues of the dog's skin.

Trans-mission

Demodectic mange is not transmissible to humans, and not readily transmissible between adult dogs. Transmission is thought to take place only from mother to pups in the very early stage of life. The pups may show signs of infection at once, but sometimes the mites may remain dormant in the tissues without giving any visible signs of their presence. This explains the sudden appearance of the lesions of demodectic mange in a dog which has obviously not been in contact with a case. It is wiser not to breed from bitches which have had demodectic mange.

Treatment Treatment is always best carried out by your Veterinary Surgeon. Demodectic mange is extremely resistant and difficult to treat, but with the use of modern antibiotics and other drugs it is usually possible to produce a great improvement if not always a complete cure.

RINGWORM

Recognition The **extremely contagious** skin condition known as ringworm is actually caused by a fungus (the most common type affecting the dog is called Microsporum canis) which invades the individual hairs causing them to break or to die and fall out.

Trans-mission The lesions caused by ringworm are rather variable and it is, for this reason, difficult to diagnose with certainty or to distinguish from other skin conditions. Typical ringworm is seen as circular lesions, usually rather pink and inflamed, with raised crusty edges. However, there may be simply irregular, smooth, bare places anywhere on the dog's coat. Irritation may sometimes, but not always, be present. The hairs at the edges of the bare places tend to be stubby and broken, and pull out easily.

It cannot be too strongly stressed that ringworm is extremely contagious, not only to other animals, but to humans and especially children. Medical advice should be sought at once if there is any suspicion that anyone in the family may be affected.

The condition in dogs may be caught from calves, mice and rats, and also sometimes from other dogs and cats (or from humans). In the case of infection from mice or rats the bare places may appear first on the muzzle.

Dogs in the country may be infected from contact with gates or fences, where calves have been scratching. The spores of ringworm can remain alive on woodwork, furniture, or upholstery for several years.

Diagnosis Diagnosis should be carried out by a Veterinary Surgeon. He may examine the dog under a Wood's glass (an ultra violet light which causes the ringworm to glow, or fluoresce, in the dark) or examine a skin scraping taken from the dog under a microscope. Occasionally, it may be necessary to culture or grow the fungus in the laboratory to confirm the diagnosis.

Treatment If you suspect ringworm always consult your Veterinary Surgeon. Never attempt treatment on your own. Modern methods of treatment, including a very effective oral drug (a tablet) now make the condition much easier to control. However, remember that it is important that you persevere in carrying out the measures that your Veterinary Surgeon advises. The disappearance of the symptoms does not necessarily mean that you have got rid of the ringworm. Great care should be taken over disinfection and beddings, baskets, and collars are better burned. A failure to observe these precautions may lead to a flare-up of infection even after many months.

TREATMENT AND FIRST AID IN ILLNESS

If you care for your dog it is important to learn to recognise the early stages of illness. Treatment given promptly is much more likely to be effective, and delay in getting proper advice does not give your Veterinary Surgeon a fair chance to help you. An observant, thoughtful owner will soon observe the small difference in behaviour indicating the onset an illness that an outsider would miss.

EARLY SYMPTOMS OF ILLNESS

Is he ill
or not?

The most common symptoms of illness in a dog are listlessness, that is to say a reluctance to leave the basket, or go for a walk, loss of appetite, weight loss, excessive thirst, excessive urination, vomiting, or diarrhoea.

If your dog is reluctant to leave his bed, it may be that he is suffering from a generalised illness, or that he is suffering from pain or injury to a limb which prevents him from getting up.

It sometimes happens that a dog which has suffered some minor injury or strain which was not noticed during exercise, will stiffen up while lying in his basket, and find himself almost unable to get up on the following day. Taking a tit-bit of some kind to his basket will usually help to differentiate between these two kinds of trouble. An ill dog will usually refuse food, but one with some localised injury (unless he is in great pain) will usually eat.

HOT OR COLD NOSE

A runny
nose

It has always been considered that a dog with a hot nose is ill, but this is not necessarily the case. A normal dog, and especially a puppy, will very often have a warm dry nose when he wakes up from a sleep. Equally, a dog with a cold wet nose may sometimes be found to be running a temperature. However, a runny nose, especially if there is a thick discharge, may well be a danger sign. Dogs do not suffer from common colds in the human sense and a runny nose might indicate the onset of a more serious condition, e.g. kennel cough, distemper, or hepatitis.

EXAMINING YOUR DOG

It is important in the case of suspected illness or injury to be able to examine your dog thoroughly. A little applied common sense would tell you whether the problem is a minor ailment or injury, which you could attend to yourself, or whether you should get in touch with your Veterinary Surgeon for advice. Unless your dog is a real heavyweight you will probably find it helpful to stand him on a low table under a good light to make a proper examination.

Restraint

If some painful area, such as an injured nail or paw is to be examined, even the best mannered dogs may snap. The best method of restraint is to use a muzzle, and it is better to apply it from the start, rather than to wait until the dog has become upset and difficult, or you have been bitten.

Muzzles

It is possible to buy leather or plastic muzzles to fit most sizes of dogs, but it is quite easy to improvise a satisfactory substitute, using a length of strong bandage. A loop of bandage is slipped over the dog's nose, crossed under the jaw, and then tied firmly behind the ears (see diagrams). The pressure of the muzzle rests on the bones of the dog's nose, and does not restrict breathing, but quite effectively prevents biting.

Tape muzzle for a short-nosed dog   *Tape muzzle for a long-nosed dog*

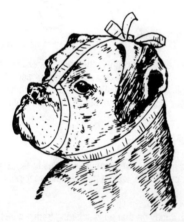 

Sedation

If you have a dog which is really unmanageable your Veterinary Surgeon may be willing to give you a tranquillising tablet to administer before taking the patient to the surgery for an examination.

EXAMINATION FOR WOUNDS

Wounds in the dog are often obscured by hair, especially in the more shaggy members of the species. If you suspect that your dog might have an injury, first clip the hair away carefully, using a pair of blunt-ended scissors if possible, and then bathe the wound using e.g. a simple saline solution. Small cuts are often found in the pads and in the web of the paw as a result of broken glass. If the wound is very small, it may be sufficient to bathe it well and then keep it covered with a bandage or clean sock for a day or two. If the wound looks large enough to require stitching, or if it appears infected or if there is a lot of bleeding, always get advice from a Veterinary Surgeon.

HAEMORRHAGE – BLEEDING

Haemorrhage may be of two kinds. The most common is venous (as the result of damage to a vein). In this, while there may be quite a lot of blood, it is darkish in colour, and the bleeding is fairly easy to control. Arterial haemorrhage is less common, because arteries are stronger and found deeper in the body, but this is much more serious. Bright red blood spurts from the damaged blood vessel and the bleeding is very difficult to stop. It is important to get in touch with a Veterinary Surgeon as soon as possible.

First aid

The best method to stop bleeding is to apply a pressure bandage. Put plenty of cotton wool over the bleeding point, and bandage firmly. Do not bathe the wound, or remove the bandage even if the blood starts to show through (see illustrations of bandage applications p. 69). Keep the patient as quiet and warm as possible.

Apply a tourniquet

In very severe arterial haemorrhage in a limb it may sometimes be necessary to apply a tourniquet to stop the bleeding. A tourniquet can be improvised using a strong clean handkerchief or an elasticated belt.

Apply the handkerchief as a tight bandage above the point of bleeding (nearer to the head) and tie the two ends. If this is insufficient to check the bleeding, slip a pencil into a layer of the bandage, and twist to exert greater pressure.

Warning – A tourniquet must never be left on continuously for longer than ten minutes. It will cut off all blood supply to the limb and gangrene might ensue which may well result in the death of the patient.

FRACTURES – BROKEN LIMBS

It is not always easy to tell if a limb is broken and an x-ray may be necessary. However, if the leg hangs limply and the animal is unable to support any weight a fracture should be suspected and help obtained as soon as possible. Try to keep the dog as still as possible. It is a help to transport the patient in its own basket or bed.

Compound Fracture - This is the term applied to a fracture in which there is also an open wound, often with fragments of bone visible through the opening. Simply cover the wound in a clean linen cloth. Do not attempt to push pieces of bone back into the wound. Seek Veterinary advice immediately.

Greenstick Fracture – This term is used to describe what happens in the bones of young animals or diseased bones. The bones are softer and tend to bend rather than shatter as they do in an older animal, with an incomplete fracture line.

TAKING THE TEMPERATURE

Normal temperature

In the dog the temperature is taken by inserting a thermometer (moistened with a little petroleum jelly) about two inches into the rectum, applying gentle pressure to lie the thermometer against the rectal walls. It is wise to get someone to help you with this job, as thermometers are very easily broken if the patient struggles. A Veterinary thermometer is a useful aid. This is rather heavier than the human variety, has a blunt end, and is easier to read. Normal temperature in the dog is about 101.5°F (38.5°C). The temperature may be raised after exercise, but in a listless dog a rise of more than 1.5°F (i.e. to 103.0°F) probably indicates the onset of illness. A depressed temperature is found normally in a bitch just before whelping, but it also occurs as a result of shock, or collapse, when it is a very serious indication of ill health.

TAKING THE PULSE

It is possible to detect the pulse in the femoral artery which runs on the inner side at the top of the hind leg, in the groin, but there may be considerable variations (62-130/minute), and it is rather the quality of the pulse beat (which can be detected by an experienced person) than the rate, which gives an indication of the dog's state of health.

SYMPTOMS TO LOOK FOR

Anorexia or loss of appetite

If a dog is generally fussy about his food, it is probably an indication that you are overfeeding him, but if a normally hungry dog refuses his food, it may well be a sign of illness. However, it is as well to check that he has not had a chance to get at a rubbish bin, or some left-over bones, before starting to worry seriously, and to make sure that there is no physical reason interfering with eating, such as a piece of stick or bone lodged in the mouth.

Cough

A cough may be a symptom of some general illness such as kennel cough, tonsillitis, distemper, or hepatitis. It can also sometimes indicate an obstruction, such as a bone in the throat, although generally the animal will become quickly distraught and paw at the mouth if a bone or stick is lodged. In elderly dogs, a soft cough is often heard as a result of heart trouble, particularly after exertion.

Coughing in puppies can be due to roundworm infestation; the larvae, during their life cycle, migrate through the lungs, before developing in the intestines into adult worms (see Chapter 5 on Internal Parasites). Because of the extreme seriousness of kennel cough, roundworms, distemper, or hepatitis in young puppies, it is always wiser to treat a cough as a possible symptom of illness, and to consult a Veterinary Surgeon rather than to attempt treatment on your own. It must be emphasised again that dogs do not get coughs and colds as a result of the common cold virus of humans, and they cannot catch or transmit human colds.

Diarrhoea & constipation

These two conditions can easily be confused. If you notice that your dog is straining, apparently trying to pass a motion, this may be due to the presence of hard faeces in the bowel, often as a result of eating bones, but it may also be due to the fact that he has passed a liquid motion, and now is straining hard, but is only getting rid of a little mucus or blood. Never administer a laxative without being completely certain which condition you are treating. Harsh laxatives such as castor oil are rarely given now. They cause abdominal pain and the immediate laxative effect is often followed by a secondary constipation. Liver, while it is an excellent food for dogs, may sometimes cause diarrhoea, so it is wise to check on the content of any tinned foods which are fed. A sudden change in diet is one of the most common causes of diarrhoea. Try to keep your dog on as stable a diet as possible, and introduce any dietary changes gradually.

Passing blood

Dogs will quite often pass blood following severe diarrhoea, but it is a symptom which should be taken seriously, i.e. it may indicate colitis or parvovirus infection, and it is best always to consult a Veterinary Surgeon.

First aid for diarrhoea

It is best to cut out food completely for 24 hours and give only small drinks of glucose and water (one teaspoonful of glucose dissolved in one cup of water). If the condition improves, give a light diet such as steamed fish or chicken, with a little brown bread or rice, for a day or two. If the diarrhoea does not improve within 2 days, always consult a Veterinary Surgeon, as it can soon lead to considerable loss of condition.

Straining is usually caused by some discomfort in the bowel, but it may also result from inability to pass urine due to some obstruction in the bladder (e.g. Stones), or to pain in the bladder as a result of cystitis. In older male dogs, straining may indicate an enlarged prostate, and in the pregnant bitch it may signal the start of whelping. If a dog has not been observed to urinate for 12 hours, advice should be sought.

Vomiting

Dogs seem to have a natural tendency to regurgitate their food on occasions and it is not uncommon for a healthy dog which has eaten his meal to quickly bring it back almost unchanged and to immediately eat it again.

Persistent vomiting

If vomiting is persistent this is a much more worrying symptom and must be taken seriously. It can be one of the early symptoms of a number of illnesses ranging from gastro-enteritis, to kidney disease and jaundice, or pyometra (see Chapter 7) in the bitch. It may also be an indicator that the dog has swallowed a foreign body, that is to say some object which cannot be digested and will soon set up an obstruction with symptoms of serious illness. In the case of puppies this may be something like a child's toy, which it has picked up from the floor, but with older dogs it is most often a chop or chicken bone, or a stone which has been swallowed while playing. Always seek Veterinary attention with any case of persistent vomiting within 12 hours if it has not ceased.

Vomiting blood

This often follows persistent vomiting, as a result of a ruptured blood vessel in the stomach. It is a potentially serious symptom, and it is wise to consult a Veterinary Surgeon as soon as possible.

First aid for vomiting

Starvation is always the best immediate policy if there is vomiting, and it is best to withhold both food and water at first. A dog which has vomited repeatedly often develops a voracious thirst, and if it is allowed access to plain cold water it will continue a cycle of drinking and vomiting until it becomes completely dehydrated and exhausted. While waiting to consult a Veterinary Surgeon, it is best to give only small drinks (about one tablespoonful every hour) of either boiled water or glucose and water (in the proportions of one teaspoon of glucose to one teacup of water).

PAIN

It is not always easy to tell from simple observation if a dog is suffering pain. Dogs in pain may adopt an "anxious expression" and breathe more rapidly. A limp is usually a sign of pain in the limb, but may equally result from shortening of the limb following a healed fracture. A dog with a slipped disc syndrome will cry out in pain but one with a serious abdominal condition will, as a rule, stand with his back arched and look wretched. Dogs cannot tell us how they feel, so it is really important that the owner who is in any doubt should consult a Veterinary Surgeon.

GENERAL CARE OF THE SICK DOG

If your dog is under treatment by a Veterinary Surgeon it is important to carry out all the instructions you are given. Tablets or medicines should always be given at the correct time. However, if you are unable to give them or feel that they are not suiting your dog, always ring up for advice, rather than waiting until your next appointment, and leaving the dog without medication meanwhile.

Warmth and quiet

As a general rule a sick dog requires warmth and quiet. See that the basket or bed is in a peaceful corner, near a radiator, or give a well-wrapped hot water bottle to supply comfort. Unless advised otherwise in a particular case, fresh water should be freely available.

Foods

Sherley's Lactol, or egg beaten in milk, is an excellent invalid food. Broth made from chicken or rabbit is usually very acceptable, and the many strained meat and fish preparations now available for babies are excellent for tempting a sick dog, as well as there being a range of prescription diets specific to various ailments.

Grooming

Dogs, like people, usually feel better when ill if they are clean and tidy, so don't give up your grooming routine. Your dog will quite appreciate a gentle brushing or combing, and any discharge from the eyes or nose should be carefully bathed and cleaned away. Blankets and bed covers should be regularly changed and washed.

INFECTIOUS DISEASES

If your dog is suffering from an infectious disease it really is important to see that he is kept as far as possible completely isolated. This means exercising only in your own garden or yard, and it is better to discourage any dog-owning friends from coming to call, as infection can easily be carried on clothes or shoes.

After a contagious disease such as mange or ringworm, all bedding should be destroyed, not forgetting the collar and lead. After a case of distemper or parvovirus, it is not safe to bring another dog (unless it is inoculated) into the house for several months.

ACCIDENTS

After a road accident, it is often quite difficult to assess the amount of damage incurred by an animal. A dog may sometimes be knocked unconscious and then quite suddenly recover, and be completely normal. Equally a dog which at first seems unhurt may collapse later as a result of internal haemorrhage. While waiting for the opinion of a Veterinary Surgeon it is best to keep the dog as quiet and warm as possible. If at all possible, get him inside, and if you suspect that there may be a broken limb try to improvise a stretcher, or carry him in his own box or basket to avoid any unnecessary movement. Cover any open wounds with a clean dry linen cloth.

ADMINISTRATION OF MEDICINES

Giving tablets and medicines to dogs often seems to present great problems to the owner. If the dog is still taking food, it is well worth trying persuasions. It is not advisable to put tablets in the main meal, as they are usually found, and the dog becomes very suspicious of its next meal. Much better to put the tablet, or halved tablet if it is a large one, into a piece of butter, cheese or meat, and give it separately as a treat – but give your dog credit for having some intelligence and carry out the disguising out of sight.

In the case where a dog is ill and off food, a more direct approach must be used.

If the tablets are likely to have an unpleasant taste it is better to put them in a small piece of cheese before giving them. Sit your dog down, preferably in a corner where he cannot back away, then open the mouth with a hand on the upper jaw, just behind the canine (fang) teeth, and with the other hand push the tablet right to the back of the tongue, as far down as possible. Hold the mouth shut, in an elevated position, until you are sure that he has swallowed. Stroking the throat area will encourage swallowing.

Liquid medicines

Liquid medicines are much easier to give. If necessary, a difficult tablet can usually be crushed to a powder, and mixed with a little water to give as a liquid. However, you should telephone the manufacturer first to check that this is OK as some tablets must be given whole. Sit your dog down, tilt the head back slightly, then without opening the jaw, pull out the pouch of skin at the corner of the mouth, and pour the dose of medicine down slowly. It will trickle between the teeth to the back of the mouth, and your dog will usually swallow quite readily. If you are on your own, it is easier to measure the dose of medicine into a small bottle or syringe, rather than attempt to hold a spoon in a wobbly hand.

Skin dressings

If any creams or dressings are to be applied to the dog's skin it is well worth carrying out the job immediately before a walk. The subsequent distractions will serve to prevent the dog from sitting down and licking off all the dressing and ensure that external applications do not become internal ones.

Administering a liquid medicine by pouring it slowly into the side of the mouth

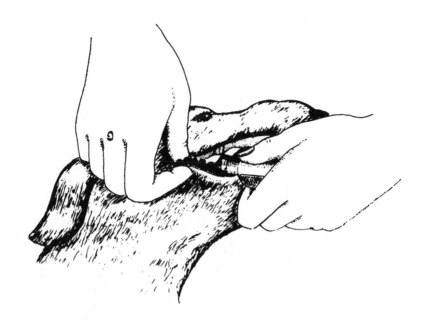

BANDAGING WOUNDS

In the wild state it is true that dogs probably licked their wounds, but there are many occasions when a bandage is necessary, to prevent haemorrhage, to prevent dirt getting into a wound, or to prevent a dog from opening up a wound that has been stitched.

Legs and feet

Wounds affecting the limbs and paws are probably the most common ones that an owner encounters, and it is a great help to be able to apply a satisfactory bandage. In dealing with the paw it is best to pack wisps of cotton wool between the toes to avoid constriction of the pads. Even when the wound is higher up the limb it is wiser to include the foot in the bandage. A constricting bandage placed half way up a limb will have an effect rather like a tourniquet, and the lower half of the leg will start to swell.

Having thoroughly cleansed the wound, apply an antiseptic dusting powder or an antiseptic lotion, and cover with a piece of clean gauze. Next apply a layer of cotton wool all over the leg to prevent constriction and bandage with an even pressure, starting from the foot. Crepe bandages are particularly good for this purpose as the elasticity helps to grip the limb. Finally, add a few bands of adhesive plaster strip, catching the hair, to prevent the bandage slipping or being pulled off by the patient, and cover the whole leg with a man's stretch sock to keep the dressing clean.

The first stage in bandaging the foot, ensuring that the injured area is well protected

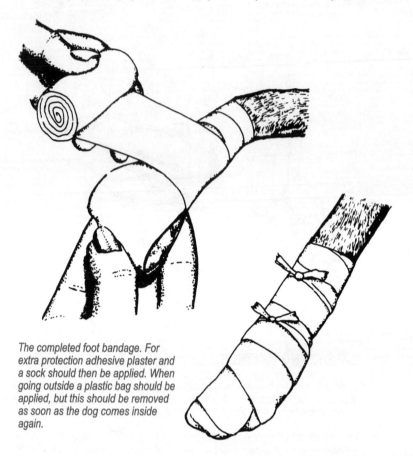

The completed foot bandage. For extra protection adhesive plaster and a sock should then be applied. When going outside a plastic bag should be applied, but this should be removed as soon as the dog comes inside again.

Tails

Tails are especially difficult to bandage satisfactorily, because the dressings can so easily be wagged or pulled off. Start with gauze and a layer of cotton wool as with the foot, but when bandaging take care to fold back groups of hairs and include them in the bandage layers to prevent it from slipping off. Finish with bands of adhesive plaster which extend beyond the bandage onto the hair of the tail.

When bandaging the tail, include hair in each turn of the first layer to prevent slippage

The tail bandage should be finished with adhesive plaster that extends onto uncovered hair

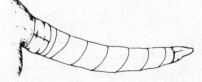

Ears

Ears are very susceptible to injury as a result of fights or barbed wire, and they tend to bleed very profusely. The situation is worsened by the dog's natural tendency to shake its head, so it is essential that the ear is immobilised by a firm bandage. At the same time care must be taken to avoid constriction of the throat, so this is another case where a crepe bandage is helpful.

Apply a fairly generous pad of cotton wool to both sides of the ear, and in the case of long-eared breeds, fold the ear back over the top of the head. Apply the bandage around the head, leaving the unaffected ear free, as a peg, or anchor, to prevent the bandage from slipping back. Finish with strips of adhesive plaster, and finally make a balaclava helmet out of the leg and welt of a man's sock (leaving a hole for the free ear) to protect the dressing, and keep it clean.

Ear bandage. The affected ear is covered, while the other is left free to act as an anchor for the bandage. Ensure the bandage is only finger-tight at the throat.

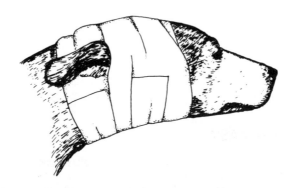

Body wounds

Body wounds can be quite difficult to deal with, and bandages are often necessary to protect surgical wounds, particularly in the abdominal area.

A "many-tailed" bandage, that is to say a broad strip of old sheet with ties all the way along, is usually effective in covering an abdominal wound. If two holes are made to take the front legs it will prevent the bandage from slipping back (see diagram). Alternatively, a child's sweater, with the dog's front legs going through the armholes, will make an effective cover for most of the body. A clean piece of gauze can be stitched inside the jacket to cover the affected area.

A body bandage suitable for covering abdominal wounds

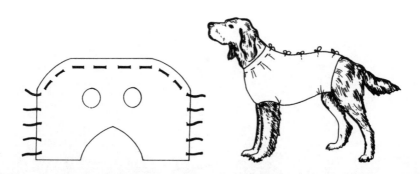

Elizabethan collar

This usually consists of a funnel of strong cardboard, or more commonly plastic, which is attached to the dog's collar, and projects forward beyond the muzzle. It is an effective way of preventing a dog from rubbing at injuries on the head, and it will also prevent it from biting at the limbs or body in cases of sutures.

A simple Elizabethan collar

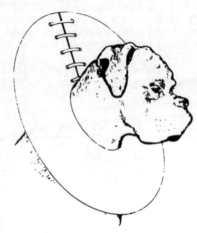

EUTHANASIA

The sad time may come when we have to decide to end the life of a much-loved pet. This is always a very difficult decision to make, and it is only too easy for a devoted owner to keep a pet alive longer than is really kind. If you genuinely feel that your dog, as a result of illness or old age and infirmity, is unable to enjoy life, it is much better to face facts and make a decision. The break will have to come soon and you may well reproach yourself if you allowed your pet to suffer for a few unnecessary days or weeks. Equally there are occasions when a dog has to be destroyed because it is unmanageable, or vicious. It is the owner's duty to see that it is painlessly destroyed, rather than to pass it on, with all its problems to someone else.

Injection

Euthanasia by pentobarbitone injection is by far the best and most humane method. Your Veterinary Surgeon can supply you with a strong tranquillising tablet which will save the dog from being frightened or alarmed when taken to the surgery or clinic. He will then be given an injection (usually intravenously) which will induce deep anaesthesia, followed by death, without any pain at all.

DISEASES AND AILMENTS OF DOGS

This chapter is intended to help the owner to recognise or understand some of the more common ailments of the dog, but it is not intended to be a manual of home treatment. It is important to remember that since your dog cannot talk, it is only too easy for the owner to be mistaken when diagnosing a complaint, and in this way the dog may, quite unintentionally, be caused unnecessary suffering. In all areas there are Veterinary Surgeons available for consultation, and in most regions there are welfare clinics, for those who are unable to pay fees. If you suspect that your pet is ill, don't delay, consult expert advice at once.

ABSCESS

An abscess is usually seen in the form of a raised, painful swelling caused by the formation of pus under the skin, and they may occur anywhere. The swelling, as a rule, will gradually increase in size and become tense, until it bursts to discharge pus and blood. There may be a rise in temperature and the dog will feel ill, lose his appetite, and may resent handling.

Abscesses often form as a result of dog, fox, or rat bites, or from the presence of grass awns in the paws or limbs.

Anal Glands Abscess – See Anal Glands.

Tooth Abscess – The most common tooth abscess is the malar abscess, which develops as a result of infection at the root of the large carnassial molar tooth in the upper jaw.

The symptoms are the development of a swelling on the dog's cheek, just below the eye. The swelling eventually bursts, but continues to fill up and form. The condition will not heal until the affected tooth has been removed, so consult your Veterinary Surgeon.

First Aid Treatment - For a superficial abscess, the best treatment is to bathe with warm water and a proprietary antiseptic or saline solution until such time as the abscess bursts. Continue to bathe the wound to keep it open and prevent healing taking place too quickly, or another abscess will soon appear on the same site. In all except very minor cases, antibiotic treatment will be necessary, so consult your Veterinary Surgeon.

ALLERGY - NETTLE RASH - URTICARIA

Nettle rash is the body reaction of a particular dog (or person) to a food, or other substance. It can best be understood by considering the fact that while many people eat shellfish without the slightest ill effect, in a few people it causes a rash or other symptoms. In the dog it is often extremely difficult to be certain what has produced the symptoms, but a reaction to a wasp or bee sting is a common cause.

Symptoms - It is usually noticed that quite suddenly the dog is covered with raised blotches. In smooth-haired breeds the skin over the head area may present an almost quilted appearance, and swelling of the gums or throat may cause the dog some discomfort.

Treatment – In many cases the symptoms disappear spontaneously after a few hours, but they may return again. Consult your Veterinary Surgeon. Antihistamine treatment will usually give quick relief from the symptoms.

ANAL GLANDS

These are enclosed in two pear-shaped sacs, situated under the skin at each side of the anus, in both dogs and bitches. They are scent glands and produce a very foul smelling secretion, which is normally discharged through a tiny, pore-like opening at each side of the anus. They may sometimes be removed surgically if persistent abscesses make this necessary. In the wild state the glands probably emptied as a result of the pressure of hard bulky material in the bowel, but with modern soft foods the glands may fail to empty and cause the dog considerable irritation and discomfort. A dog with anal gland troubles will very typically slide along the ground on his bottom, or lick and bite continually under his tail. This condition is often confused with worm infestations and it is important to be certain of the cause before carrying out treatment. In the vast majority of cases, it is anal glands and not worms which cause anal irritation.

Treatment – The anal gland can be expressed (or emptied) quite easily by a Veterinary Surgeon and this is something that the owner can learn to do, if shown. Infected anal glands may continue to produce an excessive evil smelling and sometimes blood stained discharge. Antibiotic treatment is usually required.

Anal Gland Abscess – In this case the duct becomes blocked, and the anal sac fills up with septic material. A red swelling is seen at one side of the tail and the dog is usually in considerable pain. Consult a Veterinary Surgeon as soon as possible.

ANAL PROLAPSE

This is seen most commonly in young pups, and results from excessive straining, usually following an attack of diarrhoea. A portion of the bowel is extruded from the rectum, and it quickly becomes red, swollen and painful. In some cases the bowel may become telescoped upon itself, and this is known as an intussusception.

First Aid – It may be possible to return the prolapse, but in most cases the dog will immediately start to strain. Consult a Veterinary Surgeon immediately.

ARTHRITIS

Osteo-arthritis affects the joints, more often in older dogs. Medication can provide a great deal of improvement. Sherley's Rheumatine Tablets will relieve the dog's pain and stiffness, or modern, non-steroidal anti-inflammatory drugs are available from Veterinary Surgeons.

ASCITES

This is an abnormal accumulation of fluid in the abdominal cavity. In older dogs, ascites is seen often as a result of poor heart function, but it may be possible to improve the condition with suitable drugs. Advanced cases, and those that are due to liver failure or obstructive growths, have a very poor outlook.

BAD BREATH

This is a condition which causes great worry to dog owners but as a rule, with common sense it can be dealt with. In nearly all cases bad breath is due to either bad teeth, tartar on the teeth, or a gum infection. Get your Veterinary Surgeon to remove any teeth that are decayed. Your dog will be happier and healthier without them; then keep the teeth white by regularly cleaning with a toothbrush and paste, specially designed for dogs (e.g. Sherley's Dental Range). Sherley's Breath Freshener Tablets help control breath odours, particularly when due to the type of food eaten, and a Mouth Spray is also available to freshen the mouth and help keep the teeth clean.

A piece of bone lodged in a tooth can cause soreness, and result in foul breath, but it can soon be dealt with. In older dogs, bad breath can indicate uraemia, as a result of kidney failure. This is a very serious condition, but it will be accompanied by other signs of illness, e.g. excess thirst, weight loss, excess urination. In dogs of the spaniel type, so called bad breath is often due to an infection in the loose folds of the lips, as a result of dribbling – consult your Veterinary Surgeon.

BALANITIS

This is an infection of the sheath of the penis which is quite common, especially in young dogs, and can be considered as more unpleasant than serious. There is usually a copious thick yellow discharge and the dog will tend to lick and clean himself a great deal. Swabbing with a weak solution of hydrogen peroxide will often help, but in a persistent case consult your Veterinary Surgeon.

BALDNESS-ALOPECIA

Elderly dogs do sometimes suffer from genuine baldness and, as with humans, the prospects of improvement are poor. However, if the loss of hair is accompanied by soreness or scratching, it may indicate a skin infection (see Skin Diseases). Alopecia may also be caused by hormonal disorders. All these conditions are best diagnosed and treated by your Veterinary Surgeon.

BITES

Bites from other dogs, or from rats, foxes, etc. are a common cause of wounds and abscesses in dogs. If you know that your dog has been bitten, immediately clip the hair away from the area, and bathe with an antiseptic or saline solution.

Prompt treatment can do much to prevent the development of bacterial infection. However, if the bite has become septic it is important to consult your Veterinary Surgeon as antibiotic treatment may be necessary.

Snakebites may occur in moorland areas. If you suspect that your dog has been bitten by an adder, keep him quiet and warm and consult a Veterinary Surgeon as soon as possible.

BLADDER TROUBLES

Cystitis, or inflammation of the bladder, occurs more often in bitches than dogs. The affected animal will strain frequently, passing only small amounts of urine, often blood-stained and often with a strong smell of ammonia. This is a painful condition and it is important to seek veterinary advice as soon as possible.

Bladder Stones – Stones may form in the kidneys, bladder, or urethra of dogs and bitches, as a result of the deposition of mineral salts. The symptoms are very similar to those of cystitis, but are more serious and there may be a complete inability to pass water. Consult your Veterinary Surgeon as soon as possible. An operation may be necessary, but if the condition is caught in time there is a good chance of recovery. Unfortunately, once bladder stones are formed in your dog, there is often a tendency for the condition to recur, although specialised diets available from your Veterinary Surgeon may help in prevention.

BLEEDING

The most common sites of bleeding in the dog are the paws, ears, and tail (see Chapter 6). Some dogs, usually the smooth coated varieties, may develop chronic bleeding of the ear tips or tail as a result of shaking the head or knocking the tail. This is a difficult condition to cure, and it is best to consult a Veterinary Surgeon.

BRONCHITIS

Bronchitis is usually characterised by a cough, or noisy breathing. It may occur on its own, as a complication of distemper or other diseases, or most commonly with a heart condition in older animals. While chronic bronchitis can be alleviated by drugs, it cannot be completely cured, as a rule.

BRUISES

Dogs do suffer from bruises, though they are usually only noticed if they occur on the hairless areas (see Haematomas).

BURNS AND SCALDS

Many dogs develop scorching, or even burns in the winter months, as a result of sitting too close to an open fire, boiler, or electric/gas fire. Tip: Always use a fire guard. Scalds are only too common as a result of upset kettles or saucepans and they tend to be serious, because the dog's coat holds the heat.

First Aid – Immediately soak the area in cold water, and if the dog will allow it, trim away the hair. The amount of damage may not be obvious at first, but after a few days blisters may appear and result in a very severe open wound. With bad scalds, the hair may never grow again on the affected places. Keep the dog quiet and warm as there may be shock, and contact a Veterinary Surgeon as soon as possible.

CANCER - See Tumours

CANKER

This is an old-fashioned name, which applied to all ear troubles in the dog. See **Otitis**.

CASTRATION

Castration is the name given to the neutering of male dogs. The operation is generally carried out at about six months of age from choice, though it can be performed at any age.

CAR SICKNESS - See chapter 4, Caring for your dog

CATARRH

Catarrh can be a symptom of infection in the sinuses (eg. aspergillosis), as a result of a foreign body such as a piece of stick in the nose, or due to the presence of a tumour in the nasal passages. The symptoms are sneezing, nose bleeds, or a persistent discharge from the nose. Unfortunately, the conditions can be extremely difficult to treat, and it is best to consult a Veterinary Surgeon.

CHOKING

Choking may often happen as a result of swallowing a bone or other foreign objects. It is dangerous to throw a small ball for a dog to catch, as these have been known to stick in the gullet and cause suffocation.

COLLAPSE

Collapse may be due to a number of conditions and must be dealt with accordingly. Short-nosed dogs such as pekes, bulldogs, and pugs sometimes collapse from heat stroke in summer. In this condition the breathing may be very distressed, the tongue will be a very dark bluish colour and the dog may become unconscious. This condition is very serious so while contacting a Veterinary Surgeon place the patient into a cool draught, pull out the tongue to avoid choking, and if possible apply ice packs or hose down with cold water.

Heart attacks and fits (see **Fits**) may also be causes of collapse, and it is not always easy to distinguish between the two. Keep the patient quiet and warm while consulting a Veterinary Surgeon. In many cases the duration of the collapse is brief, and the dog may appear better before you are able to get help, but it is wise to get advice on future treatment. Don't despair if your dog is unconscious as a result of a road accident. As with humans, the results are very unpredictable, and the dog could make a complete recovery.

Although very rare, dogs, or specially young pups, may be in a state of collapse as a result of eating sleeping tablets. Remember that young dogs will eat absolutely anything and see that all tranquillisers and other tablets are kept safely out of reach (see **Poisons**).

CRYPTORCHIDISM AND MONORCHIDISM

In this condition in dogs, either one or both testicles are retained in the abdomen or under the skin in the groin area. These animals may be able to breed, but it is not advisable to use them at stud, as the conditions are hereditary. In later life there is a tendency for an abdominal testicle to become abnormally enlarged and cancerous and an operation may be necessary. Therefore, surgical removal early in life is recommended.

CYSTS

These are basically swellings in the body which contain a fluid, or semi-fluid secretion. They are, as a rule, less painful than an abscess, unless complicated by infection.

Sebaceous cysts occur very often on the skin of some varieties of dogs. If large enough to cause discomfort it is best to consult your Veterinary Surgeon as surgery may be necessary to remove them.

A **salivary cyst** appears as a large soft swelling on one side of the jaw and usually requires surgery. A ranula is a salivary cyst under the tongue. Salivary cysts can be very difficult to cure.

Ovarian cysts are due to the formation of a vesicle containing fluid on an ovary, usually causing symptoms of irregular heats or difficulties in breeding. Hormone treatment is sometimes effective but surgery may be necessary.

Inter-digital cysts (cysts between the toes) cause a great deal of trouble to some dogs (see Chapter 4). They occur most commonly in dogs where the paws have a rather deep "well" between the pads where mud and dirt can accumulate. Particles of grit, or occasionally a grass seed, penetrate the skin and either form sterile cysts filled with fluid, or if there is bacterial infection, painful abscesses between the toes. Care of the paws can do much to avoid these troubles (see Chapter 4). The hair around and under the paws should be kept short, and the feet should always be well washed after exercise in muddy weather.

Treatment - Bathing the foot with an antiseptic or saline solution will usually give relief, and in many cases the cyst will burst, and subside after about forty-eight hours.

DEAFNESS

Some dogs suffer from a hereditary form of deafness, and unfortunately there is no cure for this. Deafness as a result of wax in the ears seems less common in dogs than humans, but deafness as a result of old age degeneration in the internal ear is quite usual. It is not unkind to keep a deaf animal, but extra care must be taken to avoid danger in traffic. The most noticeable fact about a deaf dog is that if asleep, it fails to react as a normal dog would when anyone enters the room.

Sherley's Ear Cleaner can be used regularly to prevent the build-up of wax and other debris in the ear.

DIABETES

Diabetes is seen most commonly in bitches of middle age, but it can occur in dogs or bitches of all ages. The symptoms are severe thirst, usually accompanied by a good appetite in the early stages, and considerable loss of weight.

Diabetes mellitus is due to a failure in the metabolism of sugar in the dog and can be demonstrated by the presence of sugar in the urine.

Diabetes mellitus can be treated by the administration of insulin by injection, but a great deal will depend on the owner's ability as a nurse in carrying out the Veterinary Surgeon's advice, as the treatment must be continued throughout life.

With **diabetes insipidus** there is no sugar in the urine, and diagnosis is less easy. It may be easily confused with other conditions as it causes thirst and urination.

DIARRHOEA

Diarrhoea may occur as a symptom in a great many conditions (see Chapter 6). If you think it may be the result of simple over–indulgence, or from eating unusual food, starvation is the best treatment. Give no solid food at all for 24 hours, and only small drinks of glucose and water (one teaspoon of glucose to one cup of water). If this checks the diarrhoea, return gradually to a normal diet, but if there is no improvement in 24 to 48 hours, consult your Veterinary Surgeon.

DISLOCATIONS

A dislocation is the name given to the accidental displacement of two bones at a normal joint. A very common dislocation is that of the toe joint in greyhounds, or of the hip joint in young dogs, when characteristically one leg will be seen to be shorter than the other. It is often difficult to differentiate a dislocation from a fracture and a radiograph may be necessary, so consult a Veterinary Surgeon as soon as possible. Many dislocations can be reduced by manipulation (under general anaesthetic), but in some cases it is necessary to immobilise the limb, with a splint or a plaster cast. In a few cases the dislocation may prove difficult to reduce or may constantly re-dislocate, in which case further corrective measures may be necessary.

DISTEMPER

This highly fatal viral disease of dogs is made even more serious by the fact that those patients which do recover are so often left with debilitating nervous after-effects. The virulence of the disease can vary greatly in different outbreaks (rather as in human influenza) and in the early stages it can be quite difficult to detect.

Due to immunisation, its incidence has reduced considerably today, but it may still occur in inner cities or the rescue dog scenario.

Symptoms of distemper usually start within 14 days of contact with an infected animal and are very variable. Firstly, the eyes become inflamed and there is usually a discharge from both eyes and nose. The dog will sneeze and cough and may develop pneumonia as a result of secondary bacterial infection. The chewing of the foot pads may occur, hence the term "hard pad" (the colloquial term classically used to describe distemper in 3 to 6 month old pups). There is often a persistent diarrhoea and in the later stages the dog may lose control of its bowel movements. At about 6 to 8 weeks after the onset of the disease, and often when the other symptoms seem at last to be improving, nervous symptoms may commence. These may start as a twitch in an isolated group of muscles or as fits, or as a gradual paralysis, shown at first by a trailing of the hind legs. In the great majority of cases these symptoms become progressively worse. The dog may go into continuous fits, gradually becoming paralysed and lose all control over bladder and bowels. From this stage recovery is very rare indeed, and the conscientious owner must consider whether euthanasia is the kindest course. Nervous manifestations can be delayed for around 2 years after a clinical episode of distemper, and the virus may be responsible for old dog encephalitis in later years.

Prevention – Nowadays, dogs need not get distemper, as the preventative vaccination is extremely effective. Consult your own Veterinary Surgeon about the correct age for vaccination (usually from about eight weeks old) and remember that it is essential to see that your pup does not come in contact with the infection before he is vaccinated. This means that he must be kept either in the house, or in a totally enclosed yard or garden, as distemper virus is extremely infectious and contagious, and can even be spread by inhalation.

Booster injections are needed to maintain your pet's immunity at a satisfactory level, so consult your Veterinary Surgeon about the appropriate time.

ECLAMPSIA OR MILK FEVER

This very serious condition is seen in bitches which are feeding pups or very occasionally in late pregnancy and is due to a deficiency of calcium in the blood stream (see Chapter 2).

ECZEMA AND DERMATITIS

These two names are usually applied to skin conditions for which there is no obvious infective agent. Skin infections due to external parasites are fully dealt with in Chapter 5. Having said this, it is still true that what we term as eczema may be due to the presence of just one or two fleas in a dog which is highly sensitive or allergic to them. If your dog is scratching, particularly at the base of the tail, with no particular evidence as to the reason, it is always worth treating him with a Sherley's flea product first.

Nowadays, skin irritations of unknown origin are an extremely difficult problem amongst dogs. It is thought that the majority are allergic in nature – that is to say that the dog is sensitive to some particular item in its surroundings or in its food, but identifying the substance can be very difficult. Wool and detergents are some of the things which have been blamed, but to eliminate them from your dog's surroundings is almost impossible. Particular foods may not suit individual dogs, so it is worth excluding one food at a time from your dog's diet, for about a fortnight at a time, and seeing if this produces any improvement. Advice concerning food exclusion diets and skin patch tests for hypersensitivity is available from your Veterinary Surgeon. In some cases it is possible to desensitise the animal.

Before assuming that your dog's skin troubles are due to an allergy, have a good look at the state of his coat. If there are mats or tangles or dead hair which need thinning out, don't be surprised if he is itchy and uncomfortable. Finally, most dogs are more prone to skin troubles in warm weather. This may simply be as a result of the increased temperature, but as this period coincides with the time that external parasites are most common, we have come full circle and can certainly say that the great proportion of dogs' skin conditions are still due to parasites, e.g. fleas and mange.

First Aid Measures – If your dog suddenly develops an acutely irritable or sore and weeping lesion it is best to consult your Veterinary Surgeon. In the meantime, it is usually safe to clip away the hair from the affected area, and protect the area either with a loose covering, or by means of an Elizabethan Collar, to prevent the dog from making the condition worse than it need be. It is wise not to apply thick, air-excluding creams to the lesion.

ENCEPHALITIS

This term is sometimes applied to the brain symptoms caused by the distemper virus (see Distemper).

ENTROPIAN

This is a congenital condition affecting the eyelids of dogs, especially Chows and Spaniels. Either the top or bottom eyelid, or both, are inturning, and as a consequence the lashes rub continually on the eyeball, causing irritation and weeping. This condition can be cured by one or several corrective operations, so consult your Veterinary Surgeon.

EYE CONDITIONS

The dog, unlike man, has a third eyelid, or nictitating membrane. This is a pinkish membrane situated in the inner corner of the eye, which is particularly obvious in Bloodhounds and Spaniels. This is a perfectly normal part of the dog's anatomy and serves as a protection in any painful condition of the eye. Many owners on seeing the third eyelid across the eye assume that the dog is going blind, but of course this is not true.

Conjunctivitis – This may result from a foreign body of some kind in the eye or from an infection. As a first aid measure, bathe the eye gently with cool water (which has been first brought to the boil to kill any germs) but consult a Veterinary Surgeon as soon as possible.

Eye Ulcers – These are abrasions to the eye surface and they are common in dogs such as Pekes which have bulging eyes. Consult your Veterinary Surgeon as soon as possible as these are not only very painful, being associated with severe blinking (blepharospasm), but can also lead to complete loss of sight in the affected eye. It is most important to prevent the dog from scratching at the eye and making the condition worse.

Glaucoma – This is a condition associated with increased fluid pressure in the eye. The whites of the eye (sclera) will appear intensely reddened. Consult a Veterinary Surgeon as treatment can improve this condition which, if left, will result in blindness. It may occur in Beagles, American Cocker Spaniels, and Basset Hounds as a primary condition and these animals may be quite young. It may also occur secondary to lens ulceration, which is more common in the older terrier.

Cataract – This is an opacity, or clouding of the lens of the dog's eye. In almost all dogs the lens becomes denser with age, and is seen as a bluish shadow at the centre of the eye, or sometimes as a greenish gold reflection in the eye in an artificial light, and this is quite normal. In most cases the dog is still able to see, though less well, and there is no need for any treatment. In true cases of cataract the lens will appear chalky white, and the dog will be blind. This may be hereditary and seen in the young animal, or associated with eye diseases, or be secondary to diabetes mellitus. Some cases will respond to surgery.

Blindness – If your dog loses his sight, it may still be possible for him to enjoy his life with a little extra care from his owner. Much depends on individual circumstances, but it is worth considering all aspects before deciding to part with your pet. Dogs depend almost as much on their senses of sound and smell as on their sight.

Prolapsed Eyeball – In breeds such as Pekes with protruding eyeballs the eyes sometimes come out of their sockets, as a result of accidents or fights. It is sometimes possible to replace the eye immediately, by lifting the loose skin above and below the eye to allow the eye to fall back into it's socket, and then applying a cold, clean compress. If not, contact a Veterinary Surgeon immediately, or the eye may be totally damaged and have to be removed.

Progressive Retinal Atrophy – Known as PRA, this is an inherited condition causing blindness in certain breeds, eg. Labradors, Golden Retrievers, Collies, Shetland Sheepdogs, Briards, Cardigan Corgis, English Springer Spaniels, Tibetan Terriers, Irish Setters, Poodles, Dachshund, Cocker Spaniels, Cairns, and Elk Hounds.

FISH HOOKS

Dogs in riverside areas quite frequently pick up fish hooks all over their bodies, and suffer accordingly. Most fish hooks are barbed, so take great care in trying to remove them. If in difficulty consult your Veterinary Surgeon. He will be able to give a local or general anaesthetic to make the job painless.

FALSE PREGNANCY

In the period usually about six to nine weeks after the end of a season, a bitch, although she has not been mated, will often show all the signs and symptoms of pregnancy (see Chapter 2).

FITS

Fits may be divided into two groups:

1. **Puppy Fits** – These are unusual and may, in some cases, be associated with roundworm infestation. They are usually only transient in nature, but it is wise to consult your Veterinary Surgeon. The puppy may seem over-excited or may fall on its side and froth at the mouth briefly. In a fit a dog may snap even at its owner, so it is wise to leave it alone, in a quiet dark room to recover.

2. **Epileptic Fits** – These are rarely seen in dogs of under eighteen months old. The fits tend to occur at fairly regular intervals, from once a year to as often as once each week. They vary greatly in their degree of seriousness, and having started will almost always continue throughout life. A dog in an epileptic fit will usually froth at the mouth, the muscles may twitch involuntarily, and the dog will fall to the ground with the legs moving in a paddling action. It will often involuntarily empty its bladder and bowel. It may appear completely unconscious and unable to recognise anyone. The fit can last from a few seconds to ten minutes or more and afterwards the dog will appear rather dazed and unsteady for a little while. Although this description sounds very distressing, tablets prescribed by your Veterinary Surgeon can do much to control epileptic fits and many owners find it quite possible to accept and live with the situation. If a dog is fitting fully for more than 10 minutes, urgent Veterinary advice must be sought.

FLATULENCE

Many dogs suffer from flatulence, or wind, after eating some particular food such as liver. The symptoms can make them very disagreeable to live with for a while. The obvious answer is to alter the diet, and for immediate treatment a Sherley's Gastrine Tablet sometimes helps.

A more serious kind of flatulence sometimes seen in large breeds of dog is due to a torsion or twist of the stomach. The dog will be in acute pain, the abdomen will be grossly distended, and the dog will stand very stiffly in one position. Contact a Veterinary Surgeon immediately.

FRACTURES -See chapter 6

These may be treated by splinting, or encasing in plaster of paris to immobilise the limb. Today they are more often repaired by internal fixation, using a metal pin or plate, or external steel fixator devices.

Dogs, and especially young pups, often suffer a sudden attack of colic or stomach pain after bolting food. Food given directly from a refrigerator can produce a similar effect. Normally

GASTRITIS - INDIGESTION - COLIC

Sherley's Gastrine Tablets will give some relief.

Some dogs periodically vomit up a little bile, usually having eaten grass, without apparently suffering from an illness.

GRASS SEEDS OR BARLEY AWNS

These get into the eyes, ears, and feet of dogs throughout the summer months. It is a wise precaution to go through your dog's coat, paying particular attention to the webs of the toes if you have been for a walk in rough grassland, and remove the culprits before they do harm.

HAEMATOMAS

Haematomas are large blood blisters under the skin and can occur anywhere on the body as a result of a knock, but they are seen most often in the ear flaps of long eared dogs. They appear usually as an oval, warm, fluctuating swelling under the skin and are uncomfortable, rather than acutely painful like an abscess. They are frequently self-inflicted, as a result of scratching at ears infected with ear mites. Very small haematomas will eventually re-absorb and disappear, but larger ones usually require surgery, or the ear will become permanently crumpled. Remember to treat the ear condition, together with the other ear, or the problem may recur.

HEART DISEASE

In older dogs, heart disease is usually due to weakness in the heart valves, which are no longer able to maintain the blood circulation at its normal rate. The symptoms are a general slowing down, difficult breathing, sometimes with a soft cough after any exertion. In severe cases there may be ascites. Treatment with drugs can produce a considerable improvement in the symptoms and prolong life, so consult your Veterinary Surgeon.

HEART FAILURE

Heart failure can be extremely distressing to watch; the dog will collapse, the mouth and gums are whitish/blue in colour, and the dog gasps for breath. See a Veterinary Surgeon as soon as possible.

HERNIA

Hernias result from a weakness in the muscles, which allows the protrusion of abdominal organs, or abdominal fat into the chest or under the skin, causing a soft fluctuating swelling. This may also occur at any point on the abdomen as a result of an accident, when they are more correctly termed a rupture. The more usual sites are:

1. **Umbilical Hernia** - This is formed at birth from a failure of the abdominal wall to heal over completely at the umbilicus. A very small umbilical hernia may do no harm, but it is wise to consult your Veterinary Surgeon in case an operation is necessary.

2. **Inguinal Hernia** - These may occur at either side of the lower abdomen in bitches. They should be repaired, because in pregnancy they represent a potential risk when the extra weight of puppies can enlarge the hernia opening. Inguinal hernia is much less common in male dogs,

when it can develop into "scrotal hernia" as the hernia contents, usually a loop of bowel, descend into the scrotum.

3. **Diaphragmatic Hernia** - This may follow an accident. The partition between the abdomen and chest is damaged. The symptoms are usually distressed breathing and a reluctance to lie down.

4. **Perineal Hernia** – This occurs most commonly in older male dogs, as a result of constant straining from chronic constipation or prostate gland enlargement. A soft swelling appears at one side of the anus, due to muscle breakdown and may gradually enlarge to form a circular area of swelling under the tail and around the anus. This is usually the most difficult hernia to surgically correct because of its situation, its cause, and the age of the patient.

HIP DYSPLASIA

This is a condition which may cause great anxiety to breeders of large and medium types of dogs such as German Shepherds and Retrievers, as the condition is hereditary. The symptoms of the condition are first lameness, and a weakness to rise, and on radiographic examination it will be seen that the head of the femur (the thigh bone) is malformed, and will not fit into the cup-shaped socket of the pelvic bone.

Whilst one can never make the hips normal, there are many types of treatment which can help alleviate some or all of the symptoms, enabling the dog to lead a happy life. They vary from simple medication to complex surgery, and total hip replacement is now a feasibility (but very expensive!). Your Veterinary Surgeon will be able to advise you of the most appropriate treatment should you be unlucky enough to have a dog with this condition.

Nowadays, most reputable breeders have the parents' hips radiographed prior to breeding as a means of screening to help reduce the incidence of this disease.

HOARSENESS

Many dogs are hoarse, or without their bark upon return from kennels. Don't blame the kennels, but try to take your dog on holiday with you next time.

HYSTERIA - See fits

INCONTINENCE

Incontinence of urine is sometimes seen in older dogs. Consult your Veterinary Surgeon as there may be many causes.

Occasionally, incontinence will be seen in spayed bitches. The bitch may wet her basket without appearing to notice. This is thought to be due to a weak bladder and usually responds well to drug therapy. Consult your Veterinary Surgeon.

Young pups may wet through excitement or nervousness, but this form of incontinence improves with maturity.

INFECTIOUS VIRAL HEPATITIS - RUBARTH'S DISEAS

This is an infectious disease, characterised by high temperatures, extreme depression, and thirst, and is caused by a virus which usually attacks the liver. It sometimes causes a characteristic blue opacity of the eye. The disease can be prevented by the use of modern vaccines and is thankfully uncommon today.

JAUNDICE

This is a symptom rather than a specific disease. The yellow colour, which indicates liver dysfunction, is usually noticed first on the inner surface of the lower eye-lid and lips. It then becomes visible on the bare parts of the skin and finally, in severe cases, colours the whole body including the whites of the eyes. It will be noticed that the urine is a very deep yellow, or brownish colour. The seriousness of jaundice depends on its cause and it is wise to contact your Veterinary Surgeon immediately, and to avoid handling your pet.

1. **Leptospiral Jaundice** – Weil's disease – This is an acute and very often fatal bacterial disease which is transmitted by rats. It is characterised by a high temperature, extreme depression, vomiting, diarrhoea, thirst, and a jaundiced colour. This easily can be prevented by the use of modern vaccines which also protect against leptospiral kidney disease. Weil's disease can also affect man.

2. **Liver Tumours** – These are unfortunately rather common, usually in older dogs. The symptoms are very much like Weil's Disease but are more gradual in onset. The outlook is very poor indeed, with the onset of ascites and weight loss.

3. **Auto-Immune Haemolytic Anaemia** – This is a disease only recently recognised. Red blood cells are destroyed and the animal becomes anaemic and jaundiced. Some cases may respond to therapy. Consult your Veterinary Surgeon.

KENNEL COUGH OR INFECTIOUS TRACHEITIS

An infection characterised by symptoms which may vary from a very persistent and harsh cough to a more severe generalised illness, including pneumonia. The condition occurs most often in boarding or other types of kennels. This is not as a result of any neglect on the part of the management of the kennels but rather because where a lot of dogs from different homes are gathered together, infections are liable to build up and spread. Vaccination is now available and many kennel owners now insist, in the dog's own interest, that a certificate of vaccination is shown before admission.

KIDNEY DISEASE - NEPHRITIS

There are two common causes: a) acute leptospiral kidney disease, usually found in young dogs and b) chronic kidney disease of older dogs.

Leptospiral kidney disease is characterised by a sudden high temperature, depression, thirst, vomiting, and loss of weight.

Chronic kidney disease may result from a leptospiral infection in youth, or may be associated with the degenerative processes of old age. The kidney is no longer working as an effective filter to eliminate waste products from the body whilst retaining the valuable substances which the body needs. The result of this is a kind of self-poisoning and the dog becomes thin, develops an excessive thirst and starts vomiting. It will usually pass large quantities of rather pale-coloured

urine which, if examined, will be found to contain abnormal amounts of protein (albumin). In the final stages the dog develops uraemia. It will vomit constantly and in spite of all this will continue to crave for water. The tongue becomes brownish in colour and the breath has a very typical foul bitter smell. If this stage is reached, euthanasia is sometimes the only humane solution.
Treatment – While kidney damage cannot be repaired, medicines and diet can do much to prolong life. Consult your Veterinary Surgeon if you suspect trouble.

LAMENESS

This is one of the most common complaints of dogs, and it almost always indicates pain in a limb, although very occasionally it may indicate a mechanical shortening of the limb as a result of a previous injury. If your dog is lame, always examine the paw first for thorns, etc. as this is by far the most common site of injury. Fractures, dislocations, sprains or strains, or arthritis may also be causes of lameness, so if you are unable to detect the cause always consult a Veterinary Surgeon.

MASTITIS

This is inflammation of the milk glands and, while it is usually seen in bitches which are feeding pups, it can occur even in young bitches. The symptoms are redness and a painful swelling on one or several milk glands, and the bitch may be off her food and be running a temperature. Consult a Veterinary Surgeon as soon as possible.

MAMMARY TUMOURS

These are extremely common in entire (non-spayed) bitches of middle age or older, and they should always be taken seriously. They may vary from a small hard pea-like nodule on a milk gland, to a large ulcerated swelling with abscess formation. They may potentially be malignant in nature (i.e. capable of spreading through the body), and it is generally considered that early surgery gives the best chance of recovery.

MANGE - See chapter 5 on external parasites

METRITIS

This is an abnormal discharge from the womb or uterus and the term is usually applied to an infection after whelping (see Chapter 2). There is usually a foul smelling greenish discharge from the vulva which may be blood-stained and the bitch will run a temperature. The condition is serious so consult a Veterinary Surgeon as soon as possible. (See also Pyometra).

MILK FEVER - See eclampsia

This condition should not be confused with Mastitis.

OTITIS (CANKER)

This general term covers all inflammatory conditions affecting the ear canal of the dog. The two principle causes of ear troubles in the dog are the structure of the ear and the presence of parasites (ear mites). In addition to these you may also get foreign bodies in the ear such as grass awns, and occasionally tumours. The shape of the deep ear canal itself predisposes to trouble. If there is any exudation, infected discharge tends to collect, rather than drain away. In some breeds such as Poodles, hair grows from within the ear canal, and if it is not regularly removed soon becomes matted, and together with accumulated wax, leads to a painful or irritable ear. In all the flap-eared breeds (notably Spaniels and Poodles), the heavy ear flap prevents the free circulation of air around the ear, and produces a humid atmosphere ideal for the growth of bacteria and yeasts.

The internal ear of the dog showing the deep canal leading from the external ear on the right

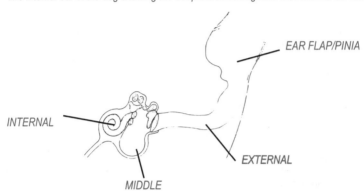

Parasitic infection with the ear mite Otodectes (see Chapter 4) causes intense irritation. As a result, the dog scratches and shakes the head, causing small injuries to the inner surface of the ear; bacterial or yeast infections follow, and if treatment is not given promptly the result may be a very prolonged and intractable case of ear trouble.

Care of the ears can do much to avoid ear trouble (see Chapter 4).

Treatment – This will depend very much on the cause. In an uncomplicated case of parasitic otitis an immediate improvement will result from the application of ear drops.

If a bacterial or yeast infection has taken place, the situation is more difficult. However, modern antibiotic, antifungal, and corticosteroid treatment can do much to help, so consult your Veterinary Surgeon.

In some cases an operation (an aural resection) may be needed to allow adequate drainage to the ear to help recovery. In extreme cases total ear canal removal may be necessary.

PARALYSIS

Paralysis results from injury to a nerve. The most common type of paralysis seen in dogs is posterior paralysis which may result from an injury to the spine, as a sequel to a slipped disc, or as a result of distemper infection when the degeneration of the nerves will continue (uncommon today), and the situation may not be redeemable. The dogs most commonly affected by disc disease are those with long backs and short legs, such as Dachshunds. The dog will be found to be quite unable to support its weight on the back legs, and if stood up, will characteristically try to stand on the fronts of the bent-over feet. There is a loss of feeling in the hind limbs and the tail is unable to wag. Depending on the site of the injury, there may be paralysis of the bladder, which is a serious complication. Paralysis may extend to the fore part of the body, in which case the outlook is very grave.

With a **posterior paralysis** the dog is inclined to drag itself around by its fore limbs if allowed, and this combined with incontinence of urine soon leads to the formation of sores. Treatment will either be with corticosteroids and prolonged confinement, or surgery, depending on the nature of the problem. The best chance of recovery is to present the dog to the Veterinary Surgeon as soon as possible, or damage to the spinal cord will quickly progress.

Radial Paralysis – This results from damage to the radial nerve in the fore limb, usually from a blow on the front of the shoulder, where the nerve lies near the surface, almost invariably associated with a road traffic accident. The dog will trail the limb loosely from the shoulder, and it will be found that there is a complete loss of feeling over a varying amount of the limb. This condition is much more serious than it at first appears. Because there is no feeling in the leg the dog will allow it to drag and become damaged, and when bleeding starts the dog will gnaw at the foot, causing terrible injuries. It is advisable to protect the limb whilst waiting to see if there is any improvement. If not, consider amputation (preferably high up the limb). Many dogs have lived happily for years with only three legs.

PARVOVIRUS

A very serious and very contagious viral condition in dogs which tends to occur in sporadic epidemics in different districts. It is characterised by acute vomiting and diarrhoea, usually accompanied by bleeding, which quickly leads to dehydration and collapse. In young animals the heart may be affected and the condition is often fatal. Fortunately, a vaccine has been developed which provides good protection.

Treatment of infected dogs is often very difficult and protracted, although it may be ultimately successful.

This virus is very persistent in the environment and may be passed by indirect contact. However, the disease is less common nowadays, thanks to effective vaccines.

PNEUMONIA OR INFLAMMATION OF THE LUNGS

This is a relatively uncommon condition in dogs. The symptoms are a raised temperature, loss of appetite, distressed painful breathing, a soft cough, and nasal discharge. Treatment with antibiotics may produce a rapid improvement, so consult a Veterinary Surgeon as soon as possible.

Pleurisy – This is usually seen as a complication of pneumonia, and is in fact an inflammation of the lining of the chest cavity and lungs. It is a serious and painful condition.

POISONING

Every year many dogs are unfortunately poisoned. They should not be allowed to wander and have the opportunity to rummage through other people's dustbins or eat contaminated bait. Tablets prescribed for humans or dogs should be kept in a high cupboard (locked, if there are children in the house). Medicines which are very helpful if taken correctly can be dangerous in overdose.
Rat or mouse poisons should never be put down in a house where there are pets. Even those labelled "harmless to pets" may well be dangerous if taken in large amounts. Warfarin, for example, which is the most widely used rat poison, is extremely palatable to dogs but causes fatal haemorrhages.

Treatment – If you know that your dog has swallowed a poison of some kind, contact your

Veterinary Surgeon immediately with details of the contents. The Veterinary Surgeon may ask you to make the dog vomit if the dog has only just eaten it. The most useful everyday substances to make dogs vomit are:

1. **Washing Soda** (though this is less common today). A piece about the size of a hazelnut should be pushed down the dog's throat.

2. **Strong salt and water solution** – given like a dose of medicine. Then keep the dog warm and contact a Veterinary Surgeon immediately, and tell him quite clearly what kind of poison you suspect.

Finally, if your dog is being sick, don't automatically conclude that he has been maliciously poisoned. Search your conscience and remember if you gave him a mutton bone a few days before.

THE PROSTATE GLAND

This is a secondary sexual gland in the male dog. It is situated around the neck of the bladder and beneath the rectum. In the normal dog it is roughly the size of a marble, but as a result of enlargement, cyst, or tumour formation, usually in older dogs, it may reach the size of an orange, or even larger. Because of its situation, there may be difficulty in passing faeces or urine and the dog often strains a great deal and shows signs of pain.

Treatment in cases of enlargement (hyperplasia), administering female sex hormones is usually very effective, but in some cases castration is advised to give more lasting results.

In case of malignant growth the outlook is poor, although fortunately this is a rare tumour.

PYOMETRA

Pyometra is a very common condition affecting the uterus or womb of bitches in the period up to nine weeks after a season. It is most common in the middle-age bitch but it can occur even after the first season.

Symptoms – The bitch usually develops a marked thirst, she may be listless and there is vomiting in the later stages. The temperature is raised and the bitch develops such a distended abdomen that the owner may suspect that she is having puppies. The reason for this distention is the accumulation of very foul-smelling pus in the uterus, and if no treatment is given, the bitch will either die of a ruptured uterus, or of toxaemia from absorbing the poison into her system.

Open Pyometra- In this case the cervix, or neck of the uterus, remains open, and the discharge is overflowing and draining away all the time. Usually the first symptom that an owner notices, is that the bitch is constantly cleaning herself, as if she were in season. There is usually a pronounced thirst, and although open pyometra is less sudden in onset, it is still most invariably fatal if not treated.

Treatment – If your bitch is showing any of the symptoms mentioned consult a Veterinary Surgeon as soon as possible. Postponement of even a day could cost your pet's life. In nearly all cases an ovaro-hysterectomy operation is needed, together with antibiotic treatment and fluid therapy. Do not delay in visiting your Veterinary Surgeon through dread of an operation. With modern methods of anaesthesia and tranquillisers your pet will suffer no pain or distress.

There is a mistaken idea that allowing a bitch to have a litter of pups will prevent her from developing pyometra. This is not the case. The only effective way of preventing this condition is by sterilising (spaying) the bitch early in life.

Rabies is a very serious viral disease of both dogs and man which is almost invariably fatal. It does not exist in Britain because of the very strict quarantine laws that have been in place for many years now.

RABIES

Rabies Vaccination – This is now allowed in certain circumstances for dogs that are going abroad. Consult your Veterinary Surgeon.

Rabies is present in most countries of the world, notable exceptions apart from Britain, being Australia, New Zealand, Japan, Malta and Cyprus. At the present time, rabies is still widespread in some European countries.

There is no cure, and immediately the disease is recognised the dog has to be destroyed.

Every precaution should be taken to prevent being bitten if rabies-like symptoms occur. In Great Britain it is a notifiable disease and all cases must be reported to the police.

RICKETS

This condition is a malformation of the bones due to an imbalance of calcium and vitamin D in the body. Nowadays, thanks to better feeding of dogs, it is extremely rare. The symptoms are poor bone growth, swollen joints, and at worst, bones that bend or fracture at a slight knock.

ROAD ACCIDENTS - See chapter 6

SKIN DISEASES - See eczema and chapter 5 on external parasites

SLIPPED DISC

This is popular term both in human and veterinary medicine which is probably used also to describe many back-ache conditions. A true slipped disc is an acutely painful condition and is commonly seen in the small breeds, particularly Dachshunds and Cavalier King Charles Spaniels.

Symptoms – The dog will often stand for hours, absolutely rigid, with the muscles standing out, especially around the neck area (cervical disc) or with a "tucked up" position (lumbar disc) in an attempt to avoid any painful movement. If forced to move it will often shriek out in pain. In less severe cases the dog will be heard to yelp as it gets up or may be unable to go up a step.

Treatment – In many cases rest, warmth, and pain-killing drugs will bring relief in a few days, but in severe cases an operation may be necessary. Sometimes paralysis will result (see Paralysis).

SCURF

This is a condition which seems to worry a great many owners. It is really just a shedding of the dry superficial scales of the skin. With a sensible balanced diet, plenty of exercise and regular grooming it should not be a problem. However, it is sometimes thought that both the perennial problem of shedding hair and scurf are probably aggravated by dogs living in over-warm centrally heated houses. Sherley's manufacture Anti-Moult Drops to develop a strong, healthy coat, dramatically reducing shedding. Anti-Dandruff Shampoo reduces the problem of "scurf" when used regularly.

If you are really worried by your pet's coat condition, always consult your Veterinary Surgeon. Simple diet additions can often solve the problem.

SNAKE BITES - See bites

SPAYING

Spaying is the surgical sterilisation of female dogs – see Chapter 2.

SPRAINS (Strains)

Sprains or, more correctly, strains are caused by the overstretching of a muscle, or group of muscles. There is usually swelling, pain and in the case of a limb, lameness, but the condition can easily be confused with a fracture, or a local infection, so it is often wise to consult your Veterinary Surgeon.

STINGS

Wasp and bee stings are very common in the summer months and cause considerable pain. If you are able to see the sting, lift it out carefully with tweezers and apply a pad of cotton wool wrung out in very cold water. In some cases the sting may produce an allergic reaction (see Allergy) and if the sting is in the mouth, as often happens, there may be considerable swelling of the tongue, salivation, and distress. Consult your Veterinary Surgeon quickly as antihistamine treatment will give quick relief and may prevent the dog choking.

TAIL INJURIES

Tails, because of their habit of wagging, seem rather prone to trouble. Some dogs develop a chronically bleeding tail (see Bleeding). Tails can also readily be sprained and even broken following a knock, and these seem to be very painful conditions. Some dogs are born with a kinked tail and while this is only a cosmetic fault, it may spoil them for showing.

TAIL DOCKING - See chapter 2 (pups)

Tail docking is sometimes necessary in the older dog as a result of injury.

TEETH

Dogs, like people, have two sets of teeth, the temporary (or puppy teeth) and permanent teeth. The full set of second teeth are usually through by six months of age. Regular care (see chapter 4) will help your dog to keep his teeth, as will the avoidance of all sweet foods which help to cause decay. If extraction becomes necessary, face the facts, and realise that your dog will be much more comfortable and healthy without bad teeth. The gums harden, and many toothless dogs can even still enjoy gnawing at a bone!

Teeth Abscesses - See Abscesses

THIRD EYELID - See eye conditions

TONSILLITIS

The tonsils of the dog are oval, pinkish lymphatic glands situated at each side of the back of the throat. In the normal dog they are very small and scarsely noticeable, but when infected they may be as large as hazelnuts in a large dog, and very red and inflamed.

Symptoms – Tonsillitis is most common in town dogs. There is difficulty in swallowing, loss of appetite, and the dog may run a temperature and feel quite ill.

Treatment – Consult your Veterinary Surgeon. Antibiotics give quick relief. Give soft and tempting foods to eat.

TUMOURS

This term covers both malignant growths (cancers) and benign or harmless growths, and they may occur in any situation on or in the dog. As a general rule one can say that growths are usually painless in the early stages (unlike an abscess) and tend to grow comparatively slowly. The symptoms of internal tumours vary with their situation and they may be difficult to diagnose. If you suspect that your dog has a tumour do not delay in consulting a Veterinary Surgeon. An early operation is nearly always advised (unless the dog is very old or in poor health), and in the case of cancer this may be able to stop them forming secondary growths elsewhere.

WARTS

Warts are really more of a nuisance than an illness, but they often have to be removed because of the dog's unfortunate habit of biting or scratching at them, causing them to bleed.

WHELPING - See chapter 2

Many people have the impression that dogs will lick wounds better, but in many cases they will

WOUNDS

actually make them worse. As a rule wounds will heal more quickly when protected, both from germs and from the dog, and this is particularly the case in any surgical wound where there are stitches.

SHERLEY'S DOG CARE PRODUCTS

SHERLEY'S FLEA TREATMENTS

Flea Collars For Dogs (Plastic)

Neat plastic collars in a range of different colours containing an insecticide giving up to 4 months protection against fleas and ticks. When worn continuously, and used in conjunction with an environmental flea control product, they can prevent further reinfestation. The collars are adjustable, available in three colours, and are for use on dogs and puppies over 12 weeks of age.

Lost and Found Flea Collar For Dogs

Not only does this collar give 4 months protection against fleas and ticks when used in conjunction with an environmental flea control product, it also works as an identification service. Each collar has its own unique identity number which you register with Sherley's direct. Should your dog become lost, the finder can ring the Freephone number which is also printed on the collar, and Sherley's will help to reunite you with your dog. These collars are recyclable, and are for use on dogs and puppies over 12 weeks of age.

Big Red Flea Spray

A highly effective aerosol spray for controlling fleas on dogs and puppies over 12 weeks of age. Best results are obtained when used in conjunction with any of the Sherley's environmental flea control products.

Insecticidal Dog Shampoo

As well as thoroughly cleaning and conditioning the coat, leaving it soft and shiny, this shampoo also kills fleas. For dogs and puppies over 12 weeks of age. Best results are obtained when used in conjunction with any of the Sherley's environmental flea control products. Available in 2 sizes (100 ml and 250 ml).

Permethrin Flea Powder

Permethrin Powder can be used on dogs and puppies over 12 weeks of age. It is gently rubbed into the coat and then brushed out. Best results are obtained when used in conjunction with any of the Sherley's environmental flea control products.

Pump Action Flea Spray

The specially designed low noise pump mechanism enables the treatment of dogs and puppies over 12 weeks of age who are worried by the "hissing" noise of aerosol sprays. Kills fleas, and can be used in conjunction with any of the Sherley's environmental flea control products to prevent reinfestation.

Rug-de-Bug

A pleasantly-scented carpet freshener that also kills fleas! Simply sprinkle on and vacuum up to control fleas in the home.

Defest II

This easily applied spray gives lasting protection from fleas and other nuisance insects in the home. One application gives up to 12 weeks control in carpets and pet bedding.

Flea Buster

An easy-to-use non-insecticidal powder that kills fleas and prevents reinfestation for up to one year in the home.

Flego

A household flea spray for the environmentally-conscious. This spray contains a short-acting insecticide to kill fleas and their larvae on contact, and an insect growth regulator for long-term control. One application lasts for up to 12 months.

SHERLEY'S TICK PREPARATIONS

Tick Away

An easy-to-use spray for the removal of ticks from your dog. Simply part the fur and spray directly onto the tick, which will die and automatically fall off within 3 hours.

SHERLEY'S WORMING PREPARATIONS

Worming Syrup

A specially formulated, chocolate flavoured syrup for roundworm eradication in puppies from 2 weeks of age. Roundworm infestations are transmitted from the mother to puppies, and therefore routine treatment is advisable. Now available in an easy-to-use pump dispenser.

Worming Cream

A specially formulated, palatable cream for roundworm eradication in puppies from 2 weeks of age. It's pleasant flavour means that it can be placed on the nose, around the mouth, or on a biscuit, and will be readily licked off. Now available in an easy-to-use syringe.

One Dose Wormer For Dogs

A modern, easy-to-use, and highly effective treatment for both roundworm and tapeworm in dogs and puppies from weaning. Requiring only one type of tablet, and given on one day, this treatment is available in 4 different pack sizes to cater for all breeds of dog.

Multiwormer For Dogs

A three week combination course of tablets for the treatment of roundworm and tapeworm in dogs over 6 months of age.

Multiwormer "Big Breed Pack"

A variation on the above for use in the bigger breeds of dogs weighing up to 88 lbs.

Worming Granules for dogs

Some dogs just do not like taking tablets! Worming Granules make the task stress-free. Just mix into your dogs food for routine worming.

SHERLEY'S MEDICINES

Rheumatine Tablets

For the relief of pain associated with locomotion and the treatment of joint disease. For adult dogs only.

SHERLEY'S VITAMINS & TONICS

Vionate

A balanced vitamin and mineral mix, specially formulated to supplement the diet of your dog. Regularly administered, Vionate can improve general health and appearance, and help assure a long, active, healthy life. This product is particularly beneficial to pregnant and lactating bitches, and to dogs in their elderly years. Available in 2 pack sizes (120 g and 500 g).

Rock Sulphur

A traditional seasonal addition to the dog's drinking water.

Calcium Tablets

With added vitamin D to assist intestinal absorption, this important mineral is essential to the formation of strong teeth and bones. Particularly valuable for young, pregnant or lactating animals.

Cooling Tablets

Cooling tablets contain a special combination of ingredients to tone and refresh the system. They can be of particular value when taken during the warmer months of the year.

Gastrine Tablets

Help balance digestion in sensitive stomachs.

Anti-Moult Drops

Moulting is a natural process for all dogs, but central heating can cause the coat to constantly shed. Just add a few drops of Anti-Moult to your dog's normal food, and see the difference.

SHERLEY'S FOODS

Lactol

Lactol is a milk food, scientifically formulated as a replacement or supplement for puppies and is also highly suitable for pregnant or nursing bitches as an addition to the diet. Lactol contains all the nutrients of natural bitch's milk, plus added vitamins, in an easily digestible form. Available in 4 different pack sizes (250 g, 500 g, 1 kg and 1,5 kg).

SHERLEY'S DEODORANTS & ACCESSORIES

Deodorant Tablets

Specially formulated to control breath and body odours in dogs. They can also help to overcome the odour of bitches in season.

Breath Freshener Tablets

Specially formulated to help provide long term action for dogs with breath odour. Tablets may be taken whole or crumbled and mixed with food.

Spray Away

A harmless spray for regular use around the home to neutralise animal odours on furniture and furnishings and to deodorise kennels, cages, and baskets and bedding. Pay particular attention to corners and crevices.

Swiftie Puppy Trainer

Has a special attractant odour, almost unnoticeable to humans. Used regularly on a newspaper or tray which is each time moved nearer the door, puppies are quickly and cleanly house trained. Helps prevent damaging accidents.

Eye Lotion

Specially formulated to gently soothe and clean the eyes. It is also suitable for use around the eyes, so aiding the removal of tear stains.

Ear Cleaner

Specially formulated to aid the removal of wax and other debris from the ear canal. It is gentle in action and does not irritate the ear.

SHERLEY'S GROOMING AIDS

Woof 'n' Go Shampoo

A 2-in-1 conditioning shampoo for dogs who like to get dirty! Specially formulated for frequent use.

Pro-Vitamin Deep Conditioning Shampoo

A luxurious conditioning shampoo, containing exotic oils and pro-vitamin B5 for a silky-soft coat.

Pro-Vitamin White Shampoo

A conditioning shampoo specially formulated to enhance the natural colour of white and light-coated dogs. Contains pro-vitamin B5, to nourish the hair right down to the root.

Pro-Vitamin Puppy Shampoo

A mild and gentle shampoo, specially formulated for delicate young skins.

Dry Revive

Freshens up dogs without the need for water. Banishes odours and leaves the coat glossy and sweet-smelling. Now available in an easy-to-use pump action spray.

Tea Tree Shampoo

A conditioning shampoo, made with Australian tea tree oil, to soothe minor skin problems and help prevent dandruff.

Diagnos Hypoallergenic Shampoo

An extremely mild shampoo, developed for highly sensitive skin. Contains Methyl Sulphonyl Methane (MSM), to aid in the relief of skin allergies.

Diagnos Anti-Itch Shampoo

For "itchy" dogs. Eases skin inflammation and irritation. Contains MSM, aloe vera and lemon grass.

Diagnos Anti-Dandruff Shampoo

For flaky and itchy skin, with dandruff. Soothes and rehydrates the skin. Contains MSM, calendula oil and salicylic acid.

Diagnos Hydrosoft Shampoo

For dry or cracking skin, causing itching and discomfort. Soothes, rehydrates, and protects against dehydration. Contains MSM, aloe vera and exotic oils.

SHERLEY'S DOG CARE PRODUCTS

Sherley's Flea Treatments

Flea Collar For Dogs (Plastic)
Lost and Found Flea Collar For Dogs
Big Red Flea Spray
Insecticidal Dog Shampoo
Permethrin Flea Powder
Pump Action Flea Spray
Defest II
Flego
Flea Buster
Rug-de-Bug

Sherley's Tick Preparations

Tick Away

Sherley's Worming Preparations

Worming Syrup
Worming Cream
One Dose Wormer
Multiwormer For Dogs
Multiwormer "Big Breed Pack"
Worming Granules for Dogs

Sherley's Medicines

Rheumatine Tablets

Sherley's Vitamins & Tonics

Vionate
Rock Sulphur
Calcium Tablets
Cooling Tablets
Gastrine Tablets
Anti-moult Drops

Sherley's Foods

Lactol

Sherley's Deodorants & Accessories

Deodorant Tablets
Breath Freshener Tablets
Spray Away
Swiftie Puppy Trainer
Ear Cleaner
Eye Lotion

Sherley's Grooming Aids

Woof 'n' Go Shampoo
Pro-Vitamin Deep Conditioning Shampoo
Pro-Vitamin White Shampoo
Pro-Vitamin Puppy Shampoo
Dry Revive
Tea Tree Shampoo
Diagnos Hypoallergenic Shampoo
Diagnos Anti-Itch Shampoo
Diagnos Anti-Dandruff Shampoo
Diagnos Hydrosoft Shampoo

Also available form Sherley's:

Beaclean Dog Disinfectant
Beaphar Dog-a-Dent Range:
Mouth Wash
Toothpaste
Toothbrush & Paste
Chewable Tablets

Beaphar Natureline Range:

Flea Repellant Herbal Dog Collar (with tea tree)
Flea Repellant Herbal Drop-on
Neem Flea-Repellent Foam
Propolis Shampoo
Propolis Foot Balm

USEFUL ADDRESSES

Association of Pet Behaviour Counsellors
PO Box 46, Worcester, WR8 9YS.
Telephone: 01386 751151
If you're having behavioural problems with your dog you can speak to your Veterinary Surgeon about a referral to a member of the APBC.

Association of Pet Dog Trainers (The)
Greengarth, Maddox Lane,
Bookham, Surrey, KT23 3HT.
The APDT can recommend a training school in your area

Dogs Home Battersea (The)
4 Battersea Park Road, London, SW8 4AA.
Telephone: 020 74937838
Probably Britain's best-known dog's home, which has cared for and sheltered getting on for 3.000.000 dogs since it was founded in the latter half of the last Century.

Kennel Club (The)
1 Clarges Street, Piccadilly, London, W1Y 8AB.
Telephone: 08706 066750
Contact the Kennel Club if you wish to register your dog. The KC can also provide a list of registered breeders in your area, breeds clubs, and registered training club contacts.

National Canine Defence League
17 Wakeley Street, London, EC1V 7LT.
Telephone: 020 78370006
The UK's largest canine welfare charity, famous for, among other things, the slogan "A dog is for life, not just for Christmas".

People's Dispensary for Sick Animals (PDSA)
Whitechapel Way, Priorslee, Telford,
Shropshire, TF2 9PQ.
Telephone: 01952 290999
Britain's largest veterinary charity providing free treatment for the sick pets of needy owners.

Royal Society for the Prevention of Cruelty to Animals (RSPCA) National Helpline
Telephone: 0870 5555999

Pet Bereavement Support Service
Telephone: 0800 0966606
Produces a very useful booklet entitled "Death of an Animal Friend" and runs a befriender service for bereaved pet owners.

NOTES

NOTES

NOTES